2.70

Date Due

DEC 14	OCT 14 '75	MAY 2 1 1980	
JAN 8	NOV 18	OCT 1 5 1980	
JUL 6	DEC 12 '75	NOV 1 5 1980	
JUL 20	FEB 4 '76	APR 1 5 1981	
JUL 26	OCT 19 '76		
FEB 5	NOV 10 '76		
FEB 23	MAR 11 77		
MAY 7	APR 1 77		
JUL 15			
AUG 20	APR 1 77		
MAY 24	DEC 2 0 1977		
MAY 24	NOV 2 5 77		
JUL 10	OCT 1 8 1978		
DEC 16	NOV 1 5, 1978		
OCT 26	DEC 6 1978		
OCT 26	DEC 2 0 1978		
MAR 28	OCT 3 1979		
	NOV 1 4 1979		
DEC 19	DEC 1 9 1979		
DEC 17	APR 9 1980		
JAN 28			
APR 16	MAY 2 1 1980		

Demco-293

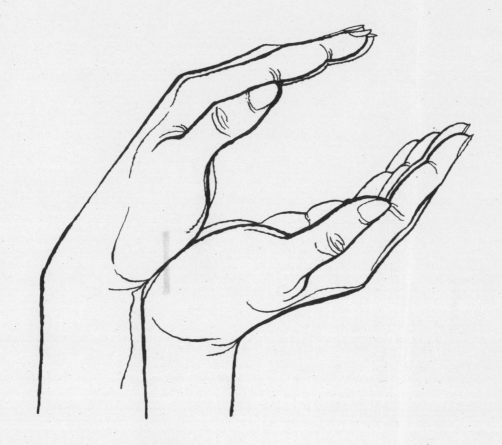

Rhymes for Fingers and Flannelboards

LOUISE BINDER SCOTT
Associate Professor of Speech
Los Angeles State College
Los Angeles, California

J. J. THOMPSON
Associate Professor of Speech
Long Beach State College
Long Beach, California

Illustrated by **JEAN FLOWERS**

WEBSTER PUBLISHING COMPANY • *ST. LOUIS* • **Atlanta** • **Dallas** • **Pasadena**

ACKNOWLEDGEMENTS

For permission to use material in this volume grateful acknowledgement is made to the following publishers and authors:

Yvonne Altman, for "Mr. Duck and Mr. Turkey."

American Childhood, for "Five Bright Stars," by Louise B. Scott.

Olive Amundson, for "Follow Me," and "The Menagerie."

Milton Bradley Company, publishers, for the following poems from *Rhymes for Little Hands*, by Maude Burnham: "Polly's Birthday," "Ten Little Soldiers," "Five Kittens," "Piggies," "Hallowe'en," "Thanksgiving," "Wake Up, Little Pilgrims," "For My Friends," "Five Little Babies," "This is the Father," "This Little Boy," "Wake Up, Little Fingers," "Striped Chipmunk," "The Fairies' Wash Day," "The Owl and the Brownies," "Snowflakes," and "In Wintertime."

Beatrice Bryant, for "Honey Bears," "Rabbits," "Valentines," and "Turtles."

Mildred Coiner, for "Ten Little Clothespins."

The Grade Teacher, for "Five Little Busy Bees." (May, 1958)

Harper and Brothers, publishers, and West, Kennedy and Carr, authors, for "Thee Thee That," from *The Rehabilitation of Speech: A Textbook of Diagnostic and Corrective Procedures*, Revised Edition, 1957, pp. 310-311.

The Instructor and Dorothy Prochnow, for "Five Strong Policemen."

Betty McAllister, for "Little Birds."

St. Nicholas Magazine, for "Ten Little Farmer Boys."

For assistance in compiling and editing Spanish poems, acknowledgement is made to Mr. James Noguer, Associate Professor of Foreign Language, Long Beach State College, Long Beach, California.

Acknowledgement is made to Dr. Harold Lionetti, Associate Professor of Language, Los Angeles State College, Los Angeles, California, for translating "Italian Lullaby," and to Mr. Alex Trejo for the translations of "With the Hands," "The Butterfly," and "What Colors Do I See?"

"I Wiggle," "Birthday Candles," "Ten Little Candles," "Five Little Pilgrims," "Five Little Valentines," "Still Time," "Readiness," and "See-Saw" are reprinted from *Singing Fun* and *Talking Time*, Webster Publishing Company.

Table of Contents

From Other Lands..........................38

Home and Family.................................77

In Fields and Woods.................................87

For Those Who
Use This Book

To childhood belongs the realm of "let's pretend." In this world of make-believe, animals talk, fairies still live in woodland glades, boxes become airplanes, and sticks turn into horses. Here, too, the magic of imagination converts small fingers into rabbits and kittens. By making a circle with his arms, the child has created the sun, or a ball, or even a snowman. Two fists placed together may be a church or a table, and an extension of the fingers will produce the people in the church or the knives and forks upon the table.

This is finger play, a type of activity which can provide a variety of educational values as well as moments of sheer enjoyment for children.

FINGER PLAYS OF LONG AGO

There is nothing new about finger play activity. Hundreds of years ago in ancient China, mothers told this tale to their children:

"Once there were five fingers, and each finger had something to say about himself.

"Mister Thumb said proudly, 'I am the best of all, for it is plain to see that I am stronger and mightier.'

" 'No, no,' said Mister Pointer, 'I am the greatest. When folks are teaching others, they use me to point out the truth.'

" 'But,' protested Mister Tall Man, 'Anyone can see that I am tallest of all. No one can begin to compare with me, for I stand straighter than any other finger.'

"Ring Finger then said politely, 'I am not the tallest, nor the strongest, nor the mightiest, but I am the only one that wears precious rings set with lovely stones.'

"Little Finger had nothing to say for a long time. The other fingers said impatiently, 'Have you nothing to say for yourself?'

"Little Finger then said, 'When God is worshiped and the hands are clasped in prayer, it is I who lead all of the fingers.'

"So, my child, it is my opinion that of all the fingers, the little finger is the greatest."

In the Rome of 50 A.D., children played "Bucca, bucca quot sunt hic?" (How many fingers do I hold up?) A manuscript dated in the year 1364 refers to the nursery ryhme, "Here Sits the Lord Mayor." The child, according to the manuscript, tapped his nose on this line. This finger rhyme, which is included in this collection, holds as much appeal for the child of today as it did for the child of six hundred years ago. The same fourteenth-century manuscript informs us that the toes were tweaked in "This Little Pig" and that the foot was slapped in "Shoe a Little Horse."

Over a century ago, Friedrich Froebel, the man who developed the kindergarten in Germany, took the games and songs of the people and adapted them for children for educative purposes. The finger play became an opportunity to integrate meanings and the emotional satisfactions of sensing relationships between parts. Many of our traditional finger plays stem from translations of Froebel, who believed that "children should be children before they are adults," that all education must have a "sense of perception" basis, and that children should be taught from objects in their own setting.

Finger plays are a part of the same primitive source from which sprang the folk tale, the ballad, and the fable; and, as a literature of the people, these plays have come down to the present time in most countries of the world. Their perpetuation appears to be due to the parent-child relationship in which mother or father and the child play together. The baby discovers fingers and toes to the rhythm of "This little pig went to market; this little pig stayed home." He finds two bare feet when mother pats his bare soles and recites, "Shoe a little horse, shoe a little mare, and let a little colt go bare, bare, bare!" Clapping hands provoke childish delight with "Pat a cake, pat a cake, baker's man!"

VALUES OF FINGER PLAYS

To the parent, finger plays are a way of helping the child move toward self-discovery and mastery over the movements of his fingers, hands, and arms as he learns to identify and locate these parts of his body as well as his ears, eyes, nose, chin, and mouth.

To the teacher, finger plays have many additional values. The manual dexterity and muscular control acquired in the earlier finger games played with the parent can be utilized and expanded into an understanding of rhythm—the rhythm of speech and music, the rhythm of life's activities. Through these action poems, children can come to know and understand concepts of size (large, small, short, tall); of shape (round, square, triangular); of place (over, under, up, down, before, behind).

FINGER PLAYS BUILD VOCABULARY. Vocabulary growth takes place through the introduction of finger plays which include material related to the courses of study. These rhymes can be integrated with social studies, sciences, language arts, arithmetic, physical education, and music. The teacher who keeps a variety of these action rhymes at hand will discover many opportunities to use them during the school day as initiating, sharing, and culminating activities in the above subject areas.

FINGER PLAYS COMPLEMENT READING. In the reading area, specifically, the finger plays in this book can be used as auditory training materials for establishing better listening habits, such as learning to follow directions; learning to hear specific sounds, words, and phrases; or learning to hear rhyming words. They can also be used as devices for developing configuration readiness and as chart lessons for the reading circle.

FINGER PLAYS AID LANGUAGE DEVELOPMENT. Finger rhymes can be used as an aid to oral language development and speech improvement, since many of them include repetitions of words and phrases that contain such sounds as "th" (voiceless), "l," "s," "r," and "f," all included among those sounds which are most commonly defective in the speech of children. For example, "See-Saw," page 133, is excellent as a game-drill for the child who has difficulty with the "s" sound. "Valentines," page 72, can be used to help the child from a Spanish-speaking background who is having difficulty putting his "v" sound in the right place. The teacher should refer to *Talking Time* (Webster Publishing Company, 1951) for further guidance in utilizing these materials for speech development and improvement.

FINGER PLAYS FACILITATE SELF-EXPRESSION. One of the greatest values of finger plays lies in the fact that they are an avenue of self-expression. The small child discovers that he has arms, hands, and fingers which will obey his commands. He finds a satisfactory outlet for emotional stress through dramatic play, using these parts of his body. The teacher may develop children's creativity by encouraging them, through the medium of creative dramatics, to act out the situations described in many of the finger plays. The pantomimic activity in the materials is as endless as the teacher's imagination.

FINGER PLAYS HELP TEACH NUMBER CONCEPTS. Finger plays and counting rhymes are not designed to teach children to count by using their fingers, although these rhymes have been misused in this way in the past. In rhymes which include numbers, it is the concept of the number which is being taught and not an automatic routine that involves ticking off numbers on the fingers. In following the parent or teacher, children forget that their fingers are just fingers. They are three squirrels, or five soldiers, or ten circus wagons. They are objects as concrete as youthful imagination can produce.

FINGER PLAYS PROVIDE RELAXATION. Finger plays can brighten the quiet time for children. Many of the poems which have become traditional in our family life were used, and still are used, to quiet the crying baby or to occupy the bedtime story period with a relaxing, rhythmic activity. The tension which produces "wiggles" and unrest seems to dissipate itself in the concentrated interest and enjoyment of the finger play.

Little eyes and eager minds are alert and absorbed as they strive to imitate the actions of the teacher. Who is to say that this tiny hand with two fingers extended is not a "bunny with ears so funny"?

PURPOSE OF THIS FINGER PLAY BOOK

This collection of finger plays was developed because those individuals who work with pre-school and primary grade children have expressed again and again a need for additional materials of this type. The authors have written a rich variety of new rhymes for fingers and flannelboards to be used for birthdays, for holidays, and for curriculum units on the circus, the zoo, the farm, home and community, the seasons, transportation, and pets. They have written rhymes to be used in building number concepts, in encouraging relaxation, in developing muscle control. They have composed some rhymes whose only excuse for existence is to provide fun for the boys and girls who use them.

Many finger plays already in existence have been included. An effort was made to trace the so-called "traditional" finger plays back to their original authors and to give credit to these authors whenever possible.

This collection includes a number of rhymes in other languages. Some are traditional and some were written especially for this book. These finger rhymes can be used to foster an appreciation of the languages of other lands or as motivation for discussions on intercultural understanding. They may be used, also, to initiate a study of a foreign language, such as is now being carried on in many elementary school districts.

SUGGESTIONS FOR TEACHING FINGER PLAYS

Teaching finger play requires a number of simple techniques. Although each game has certain individual elements, the following list of suggestions will help the teacher in presenting any finger play material.

1. If you are facing the child or a group of children, you should mirror the actions which you wish the child to perform. For example, if you wish to have the child use his right hand, you should hold up your left hand. Children will tend to move in the same direction as the demonstrator facing them. The teacher, then, must make his movements in the reverse of those expected from the group.

2. Be aware, too, of the fact that there will be children in the group who may be left-handed. These children may perform certain of the right-handed movements in an awkward manner. If you sense a coordination problem, suggest to the child that he, too, face the class.

3. Have the children follow only the action until they understand what they are to do during the rhyme. After they have played the "game" once, they will be able to say a few of the words after you.

4. Provide for several repetitions of each finger play before going on to another. Children will need to repeat the rhyme in order to learn it. As the rhyme becomes more familiar, children will ask to do it over and over again. Certain of the finger plays will, undoubtedly, become favorites and will be called for many times.

5. After the children have become familiar with a finger play, you may choose to introduce some variations: have children make and use finger ring puppets or stick puppets while saying the rhyme; use a flannelboard, if the selection is appropriate for flannelboard use; let children dramatize the action or participate in creative play based upon the rhyme; use the finger play as a chart-reading lesson; create independent seat work activities based upon the finger play.

6. Have fun yourself with these finger plays, and the child will respond to your enthusiasm.

DEVICES USED WITH FINGER PLAYS

Finger ring puppets are small replicas of the animals, birds, or objects referred to in the finger play. They are pasted onto strips of paper which are made into rings that fit the finger tips. Puppets can be brought into view or hidden from sight by bending or straightening the fingers.

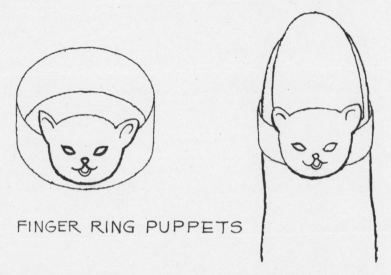

FINGER RING PUPPETS

Stick puppets can be used with much of the finger play material. The figures desired should be cut from heavy paper or backed with cardboard. Glue or thumbtack these figures to small dowel sticks or tongue depressors. A table top will serve as a puppet stage. The children using the puppets crouch down out of sight, holding the sticks so that only the figures show above the table.

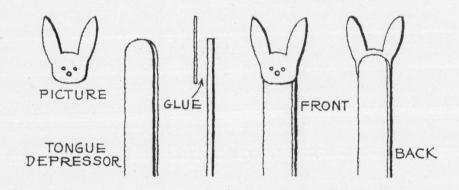

PICTURE GLUE FRONT

TONGUE DEPRESSOR BACK

The teacher may use stick puppets effectively during a finger play by mounting them on pointed wooden meat skewers. These skewers are inserted into the holes in a strip of corrugated cardboard where they will remain upright as the finger play is said.

Flannelboards are devices that can be used with cutouts to help children visualize finger plays. A flannelboard can be made by covering a large piece of heavy cardboard or plywood with flannel, suede, or felt. Flannel is preferred, since it can be colored or painted more easily to represent a scene. Also, flannel has more nap than felt or suede. Small bits of flannel or sandpaper can be pasted on the backs of the pictures which are to be used on the board. Outline figures of felt will adhere to the board in a more satisfactory manner. These figures or pictures are placed upon the board or removed from it as suggested by the characters or action of the finger plays.

FLANNEL
OR
SANDPAPER

BIRTHDAYS

"What fun!" the children will say if the teacher recognizes each birthday with a special finger play!

Here are the beginnings of arithmetic and number concepts as children discuss ages and birthdates.

A Birthday

Today is . . . .'s birthday;
Insert the name of the child.
Let's make her (him) a cake;
Mix and stir,
Action of stirring.
Stir and mix,
Then into the oven to bake.
Pretend to hold cake in two hands.
Here's our cake so nice and round;
Make a circle with arms.
We frost it pink and white;
Action of spreading frosting.
We put six (*any number*) candles on it,
To make a birthday light.

● To use this poem with the flannelboard, you will need a felt cake and candles or similar paper objects backed with flannel. Place the cake on the board on an appropriate line and add the number of candles needed.

● Substitute the name of a child in the class who is having a birthday.

Polly's Birthday

Polly had a birthday;
Polly had a cake;
Make circle with arms.
Polly's mother made it;
Action of stirring.
Polly watched it bake.
Frosting on the top,
Right hand held out, palm down.
Frosting in between;
Left hand moves under right palm.
Oh, it was the nicest cake
That you have ever seen!
Polly had some candles,
1, 2, 3, 4, 5;
Hold up fingers one at a time.
Who can tell how many years
Polly's been alive?

—*Maude Burnham*

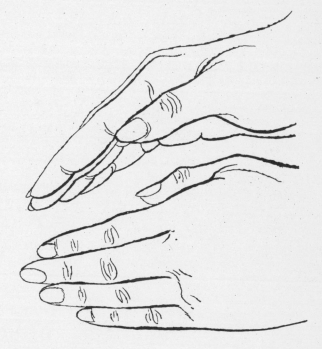

The following lines may be used for six-year-olds instead of the last four lines of the poem:

Polly had some candles;
Count them now with me;
1, 2, 3, 4, 5, 6 candles
Pop up fingers one at a time.
Do I see!

• For children who are six or
seven, use six or seven candles
rather than five.

Flannelboard materials needed
are a cake and seven candles.

My Birthday Cake

My birthday cake is pink and white;
Make a circle with arms.
The lighted candles make it bright;
1, 2, 3, 4, 5 pink candles!
Hold up fingers one by one to represent candles.
What a pretty sight!

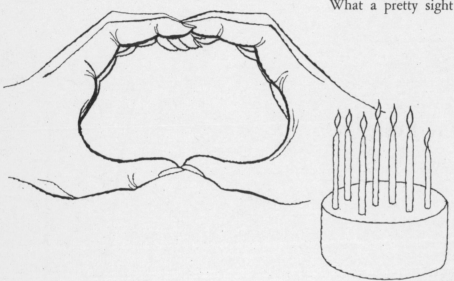

Birthday Candles

• A different number can be
substituted in line two to match
the age of any child having a
birthday.

Flannelboard materials needed
are a cake and seven candles.

SOLO: Today I have a birthday;
I'm six years old, you see;
And here I have a birthday cake,
Make a circle with thumbs and forefingers.
Which you may share with me.
First we count the candles;
Count them, every one.

ALL: One, two, three, four, five, six.
Hold up fingers one by one.
The counting now is done.

SOLO: Let's snuff out the candles;
Out each flame will go . . .

ALL: "Wh . . . Wh . . . Wh . . . Wh . . .
Bend down fingers one at a time as you blow on them.
Wh . . . Wh . . ."
As one by one we blow!

Six Little Candles

Six little candles on a birthday cake;
    Hold up six fingers.
The flames look so alive.
You may blow one candle out!
Wh! And that leaves five!
    Bend down one finger.

Five little candles on a birthday cake;
    Hold up five fingers.
Just five, and not one more.
You may blow one candle out!
Wh! And that leaves four!
    Bend down one finger.

Four little candles on a birthday cake,
    Hold up four fingers.
As gay as they could be.
You may blow one candle out!
Wh! And that leaves three!
    Bend down one finger.

Three little candles on a birthday cake,
    Hold up three fingers.
Standing straight and true.
You may blow one candle out!
Wh! And that leaves two!
    Bend down one finger.

Two little candles on a birthday cake,
    Hold up two fingers.
Helping us have fun.
You may blow one candle out!
Wh! And that leaves one!
    Bend down one finger.

One little candle on a birthday cake;
It knows its task is done.
You may blow this candle out!
Wh! And that leaves none!
    Place hands behind back.

● "Wh" is a two-letter consonant speech sound which appears in such words as *white, what, when,* and *where.* See *Talking Time,* p. 194, for instructions on producing this sound.

Flannelboard materials needed are a cake and six candles.

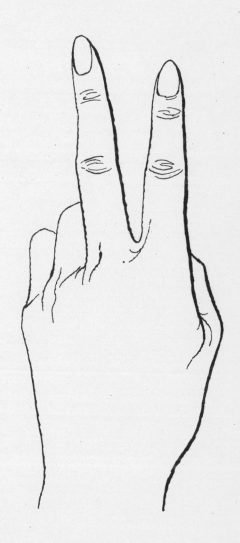

● Caution: do not voice the "wh" sound as "whuh." Use "The Pin Wheel Sound," *Talking Time,* p. 194.

Flannelboard materials needed are ten candles—three red, three white, and four blue.

Ten Little Candles

Ten little candles on a chocolate cake;
>Hold up both hands with fingers extended.

"Wh! Wh!" Now there are eight!
>Bend down two fingers.

Eight little candles on a candlestick;
"Wh! Wh!" Now there are six!
>Bend down two fingers.

Six little candles, and not one more;
"Wh! Wh!" Now there are four!
>Bend down two fingers.

Four little candles, red, white, and blue;
"Wh! Wh!" Now there are two!
>Bend down two fingers.

Two little candles standing in the sun;
"Wh! Wh!" Now there are none!
>Close hands into fists.

Five Brown Pennies

Five brown pennies in my purse;
>Hold up five fingers.

This one's for some gum;
>Point to thumb.

This one's for a lollipop;
>Point to pointer finger.

This one's for a drum.
>Point to middle finger.

These I'll save inside my purse,
>Point to ring and little fingers.

Until your birthday comes!

THE CIRCUS AND THE ZOO

Playing animal roles is a favorite form of childhood make-believe. A wide variety of dramatic play and rhythmic activities can result from the finger plays in this section. They can be used to extend oral language experiences in the social studies program and to stimulate creative experiences in art, music, and written language.

● This poem may be used in several different ways: (1) Have children choose which animals they wish to draw and color and let them hold these animals up as the poem is said; (2) Use the poem as a reading chart for second or third grades; (3) Use it for choric speaking, giving two lines to each child. The first two lines and the last two lines are said in unison.

Flannelboard materials needed are felt animals named in the poem.

Ten Circus Wagons

Ten circus wagons, painted oh, so gay,
Came into town with the circus today!
Hold up ten fingers.
This one holds a lion
That gives a big, loud roar!
Point to thumb on opposite hand.
This one holds a tiger
Fast asleep upon the floor;
Point to pointer finger.
This one holds a funny seal
That nods to left and right;
Point to middle finger.
This one holds a zebra
That is striped all black and white;
Point to ring finger.
This one holds a camel
With two humps upon his back;
Point to little finger.
This one holds a panther
With his coat of fur so black;
Point to thumb on other hand.
This one holds an elephant
That is drinking from a pail;
Point to pointer finger.
This one holds a monkey
That is swinging by his tail;
Point to middle finger.
This one holds a hippo
With a grin so very wide;
Point to ring finger.
This one holds a leopard
With a gaily spotted hide.
Point to little finger.
Ten circus wagons, painted oh, so gay,
Came into town with the circus today!
Hold up ten fingers.

This Little Clown

This little clown is fat and gay;
> Hold up thumb.

This little clown does tricks all day;
> Hold up pointer finger.

This little clown is tall and strong;
> Hold up middle finger.

This little clown sings a funny song;
> Hold up ring finger and wiggle it.

This little clown is wee and small,
> Hold up little finger.

But he can do anything at all!

● Flannelboard materials needed are a fat clown, a clown doing a trick, a tall clown, a singing clown, and a tiny clown.

Riding the Merry-Go-Round

Ride with me on the merry-go-round,
Around and around and around;
> Move one hand in circles.

Up go the horses, up!
> Raise arms in the air.

Down go the horses, down!
> Lower arms.

You ride a horse that is white;
> Point to neighbor.

I ride a horse that is brown;
> Point to self.

Up and down on the merry-go-round,
> Raise and lower arms; then move one hand in circles.

Our horses go round and round.

● This poem may be used for a reading lesson with second and third grades.

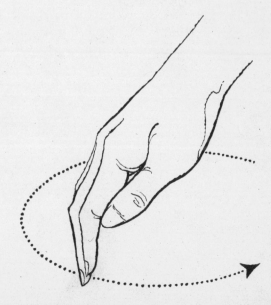

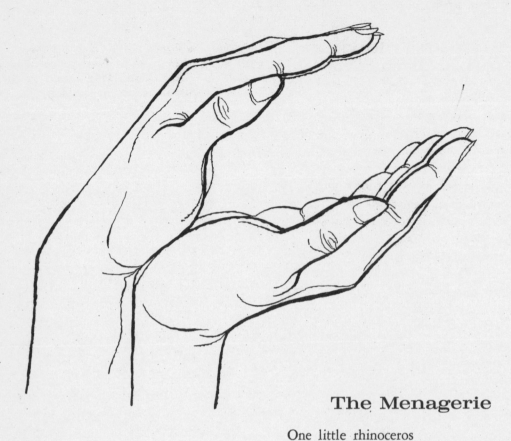

The Menagerie

One little rhinoceros
   Yawns politely with no fuss.
     Ho-hum!
       Children yawn.
Two little elephants
   In a very dainty dance.
     Brrrr-ump, brrrr-ump!
       Slap palms on desk.
Three little tiger cats
   Waiting for some friendly pats.
     Pad, pad, pad!
       Thump hands on chest.
Four little crocodiles
   With big and wide and happy smiles.
     Aaaa-p, aaaa-p!
       Snap hands together like jaws.
Five little kangaroos
   Breaking in five pairs of shoes.
     Thump, thump, thump!
       Strike fist against open palm.

—*Olive Amundson*

● Flannelboard materials needed are one rhinoceros, two elephants, three tigers, four crocodiles, and five kangaroos.

16

Counting at the Zoo

One, one; the zoo is lots of fun!
> Hold up hands with fingers extended; bend down one finger.

Two, two; see a kangaroo!
> Bend down one finger.

Three, three; see a chimpanzee!
> Bend down one finger.

Four, four; hear the lions roar!
> Bend down one finger.

Five, five; watch the seals dive!
> Bend down one finger.

Six, six; there's a monkey doing tricks!
> Bend down one finger.

Seven, seven; elephants eleven!
> Bend down one finger.

Eight, eight; a tiger and his mate!
> Bend down one finger.

Nine, nine; penguins in a line!
> Bend down one finger.

Ten, ten; I want to come again!
> Bend down one finger; then clap hands.

● As a variation, use flash cards with number names so that children may learn these sight words.

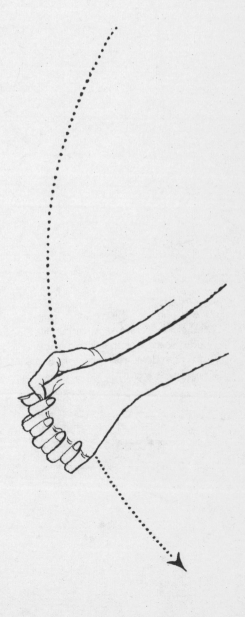

The Elephant

The elephant has a trunk for a nose,
And up and down is the way it goes;
> Clasp hands together, extend arms, and raise and lower them.

He wears such a saggy, baggy hide!
> Relax body.

Do you think two elephants would fit inside?
> Hold up two fingers.

● This poem may be used for dramatic play by having individual children dramatize each of the animals.

Animals

This is the way the elephant goes,
With curly trunk instead of a nose.
<blockquote>Clasp hands together, extend arms, and move them back and forth.</blockquote>
The buffalo, all shaggy and fat,
Has two sharp horns in place of a hat.
<blockquote>Place pointer fingers on forehead.</blockquote>
The hippo with his mouth so wide
Lets you see what is inside.
<blockquote>Place hands together and open and close them to simulate mouth movements.</blockquote>
The wiggly snake upon the ground
Crawls along without a sound.
<blockquote>Weave hands back and forth.</blockquote>
But monkey see and monkey do
Are the funniest animals in the zoo!
<blockquote>Place thumbs in ears and wiggle hands.</blockquote>

● Continue this game, using other movements, rhyming or otherwise. Use this action game to precede a rest time or as a readiness activity.

Monkey See, Monkey Do

A little monkey likes to do
Just the same as you and you;
When you sit up very tall,
Monkey sits up very tall;
When you pretend to throw a ball,
Monkey pretends to throw a ball;
When you try to touch your toes,
Monkey tries to touch his toes;
When you move your little nose,
Monkey moves his little nose;
When you jump up in the air,
Monkey jumps up in the air;
When you sit down in a chair,
Monkey sits down in a chair.

CITY SIGHTS

One sees many things in the community in which he lives, regardless of its size or location. There are planes and trains, soldiers and sailors, community helpers of all kinds. Here is a vast resource area for pantomime and dramatic play.

● Flannelboard materials needed are an engine, a coal car, a boxcar, a mail car, and a caboose.

Here is the Engine

Here is the engine on the track;
> Hold up thumb.

Here is the coal car, just in back;
> Hold up pointer finger.

Here is the boxcar to carry freight;
> Hold up middle finger.

Here is the mail car. Don't be late!
> Hold up ring finger.

Way back here at the end of the train
> Hold up little finger.

Rides the caboose through the sun and the rain.

Railroad Train

One is the engine, shiny and fine;
It pulls the coaches all in a line.
> Hold up one finger.

Two is the baggage car, big and strong;
It carries suitcases and trunks along.
> Hold up two fingers.

Three is the express car with double locks;
Send what you wish in a package or box.
> Hold up three fingers.

Four is the mail car—red, white, and blue;
It carries letters to me and to you.
> Hold up four fingers.

Five is the passenger car, so gay;
It carries people both night and day.
> Hold up five fingers.

Six is the Pullman with berths one and two,
Where we can sleep the whole night through.
> Hold up six fingers.

Seven is the dining car with tables so neat;
It's where I go when I want to eat.
> Hold up seven fingers.

Eight is the observation car that gives a wide view;
It lets you see the countryside as you pass through.
> Hold up eight fingers.

This is the train all ready to go,
Through sunshine, wind, and rain, and snow.

The Airplane

The airplane has great big wings;
> Arms outstretched.

Its propeller spins around and sings,
> Make one arm go around.

"Vvvvvv!"

The airplane goes up;
> Lift arms.

The airplane goes down;
> Lower arms.

The airplane flies high
> Arms outstretched, turn body around.

Over our town!

My Soldiers

Attention, attention, Company A;
My fingers are playing soldier today;
> Hold up ten fingers.

Attention, attention, Company B;
All salute, 1, 2, 3;
> Hand at forehead in salute.

The trumpet blows, too, too, too!
> Hand at mouth.

My fingers march as soldiers do,
> Motion of marching.

In a straight line, don't you see?
Company A and Company B,
Turn around; keep in step;
> Move fingers left and right.

Off we go—hep, hep, hep!
> Move hands behind back.

My finger soldiers every day
The general's commands obey.

Ten Little Soldiers

Ten little soldiers standing in a row.
> Hold up ten fingers.

First, they bow to the captain, so.
> Bend fingers.

They march to the left,
> Move fingers to left.

They march to the. right,
> Move fingers to right.

And then they all stand ready to fight!
> Move fingers back to center.

Along came a man with a big, long gun!
> Measure length with hands.

Do you think those little soldiers would run?
NO, NOT ONE!
> Hold up fingers again.

—Maude Burnham

Marching Soldiers

We are little soldiers,
Standing in a row;
> Children stand.

Marching and saluting,
> Children mark time in place and salute.

Round and round we go;
> Children march in small circles.

We are little soldiers,
Standing very tall;
> Children continue marking time.

Turn about together,
Marching one and all!
> Children turn in full circle.

Ten Little Sailors

Ten little sailors standing in a row;
> Hold up ten fingers.

Ten little sailors salute just so;
> Bend fingers.

They sail to the east;
> Move fingers to left.

They sail to the west;
> Move fingers to right.

Then back to the country they like best.
Where is this? Can you say?
> Move fingers back to center.

Why, back to the good old U. S. A.!
> Point to flag in room.

● Flannelboard materials needed are ten sailors and an American flag.

Five Little Sailors

Five little sailors putting out to sea,
Rocking in their little boat,
> Lace fingers and rock back and forth.

As happy as can be.
One is short and fat;
> Hold up thumb.

The ship's cook is he;
Every day he cooks the meals, one, two, and three.
> Pop up three fingers one at a time.

One is the navigator,
> Hold up pointer finger.

With a compass in his hand;
He tells about the weather, and he tells us where to land.
> Hold up middle finger.

One is the captain,
The bravest of them all;
He gives us our directions, and we hurry to his call.
The first mate is next in line,
> Hold up ring finger.

And then the cabin boy.
> Hold up little finger.

Heave ho! Off they go, shouting, "Ship ahoy!"

● Flannelboard figures needed are a short, fat sailor in a cook's apron and chef's hat, a sailor holding a compass or ship's wheel, a sea captain, a first mate, and a cabin boy.

● Flannelboard materials needed are a bakery truck, baker man, doughnuts, cookies, cinnamon rolls, pies, and bread.

The Baker Man

The baker man's truck comes down the street
Filled with everything good to eat;
Two doors the baker man opens wide;
  Stretch arms apart.
Now, let us look at the shelves inside.
What do you see? What do you see?
  Hands over eyes.
Doughnuts and cookies for you and me;
  Make circles with thumbs and pointer fingers.
Cinnamon rolls,
  Make larger circles.
And pies,
  Make even larger circles.
And bread, too;
What will he sell to me and to you?

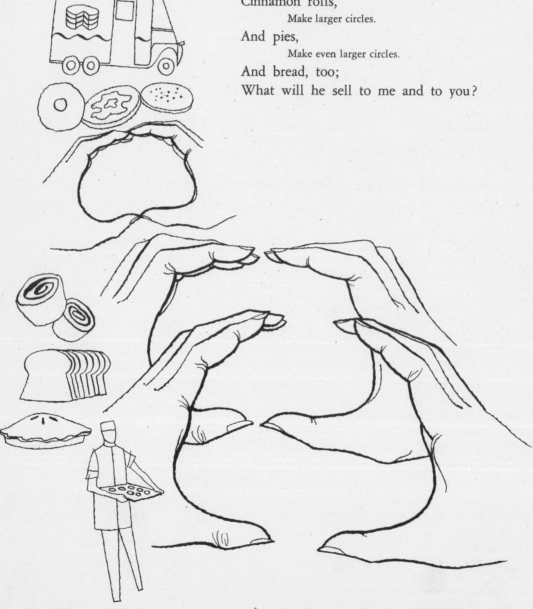

Five Strong Policemen

● Flannelboard materials needed are five policemen.

Five strong policemen standing by a store.
> Hold up hand, fingers extended.

One became a traffic cop, and then there were four.
> Bend down thumb.

Four strong policemen watching over me.

One took home a lost boy, and then there were three.
> Bend down one finger.

Three strong policemen dressed all in blue.

One stopped a speeding car, and then there were two.
> Bend down another finger.

Two strong policemen—how fast they can run!

One caught a bad man, and then there was one.
> Bend down another finger.

One strong policeman saw some smoke one day.

He called the firemen who put out the fire right away.

—Dorothy Prochnow

Five Little Firemen

● Flannelboard materials needed are five firemen and a fire truck.

Five little firemen sit very still
> Hold up five fingers.

Until they see a fire on top of the hill;

Number one rings the bell, ding-dong;
> Bend down thumb.

Number two pulls his big boots on;
> Bend down pointer finger.

Number three jumps on the fire engine red;
> Bend down middle finger.

Number four puts a red fire hat on his head;
> Bend down ring finger.

Number five drives the red fire truck to the fire,
> Bend down little finger.

As the big yellow flames go higher and higher.
> Spread arms.

Whoooooo-ooooo! Whoooooo-ooooo! hear the fire truck say,
> Imitate siren.

As all of the cars get out of the way.

Shhhhh! goes the water from the fire hose spout,
> Rub palms together.

And quicker than a wink the fire is out!
> Clap hands.

THE FARM

The farm, with its animals and activities, has long held a deep fascination for children, and the rhymes in this section will give children a chance to enjoy the wonders of the farm through finger play.

The teacher should look for opportunities to turn these finger plays into dramatic play experiences which will open up a world of creative expression for children.

On the Farm

Here is hungry piggie snout;
> Hold up thumb.

He'd better stop eating, or his tail will pop out!
Here is busy Mother Hen;
> Hold up pointer finger.

She likes to scratch for her chickens ten.
Here is a patient, friendly cow;
> Hold up middle finger.

She's eating hay from a big haymow.
Here is Baa-Baa, a woolly sheep;
> Hold up ring finger.

Her wool keeps me warm while I am asleep.
Here is funny, fuzzy cat;
> Hold up little finger.

She likes to chase a mouse or rat.
> Move fingers to imitate a running cat.

● Flannelboard figures needed are a pig, a hen, ten chicks, a cow, a sheep, a cat, and a mouse.

Ten Little Ducklings

Ten little ducklings,
> Move hands back and forth in waddling motion.

Dash, dash, dash!
Jumped in the duck pond,
> Motion of jumping.

Splash, splash, splash!
When the mother called them,
"Quack, quack, quack,"
Ten little ducklings
Swam right back.
> Motion of swimming.

Fuzzy Ducklings

Ten fuzzy ducklings
> Hold up ten fingers.

Swimming in the lake,
Quack, quack, quack!
They give their heads a shake.
> Wiggle fingers.

Bang! Bang! Bang!
> Clap hands three times.

Goes Tommy's toy gun,
And away to their mother
The little ducklings run.
> Place hands behind back.

Five Little Goslings

- The word *gosling* may be changed to *duckling*.

Flannelboard figures needed are five goslings or ducklings.

One little gosling, yellow and new,
Hold up one finger.
Had a fuzzy brother, and that made two.
Hold up two fingers.
Two little goslings now you can see;
They had a little sister, and that made three.
Hold up three fingers.
Four little goslings went to swim and dive;
They met a little neighbor, and that made five.
Hold up five fingers.
Five little goslings; watch them grow!
Spread hands wide apart.
They'll turn into fine, big geese, you know!

The Goose Family

- This poem will help teach the combination *three and two* and the number *five*.

Flannelboard figures needed are a gander, a goose, and three goslings.

Mr. Gander and Mrs. Goose,
Hold up thumb and pointer finger on one hand.
And their goslings, one, two, three,
Hold up other three fingers on other hand.
Are two and three, which make, you see,
A happy family.
Said Mr. Gander to Mrs. Goose,
Bend down thumb and pointer finger.
"The water's fine, I see;
We'll both go swimming, you and I,
With our babies, one, two, three!"
Bend down other three fingers.

Five Little Chickens

Five little chickens by the old barn door;
> Hold up five fingers.

One saw a beetle, and then there were four.
> Bend down one finger.

Four little chickens under a tree;
One saw a cricket, and then there were three.
> Bend down one finger.

Three little chickens looked for something new;
One saw a grasshopper; then there were two.
> Bend down one finger.

Two little chickens said, "Oh, what fun!"
One saw a ladybug; then there was one.
> Bend down one finger.

One little chicken began to run,
For he saw a katydid; then there were none!
> Bend down one finger.

● Flannelboard figures needed are five chicks. You may want the children to draw and cut out the insects. Use this poem for nature study.

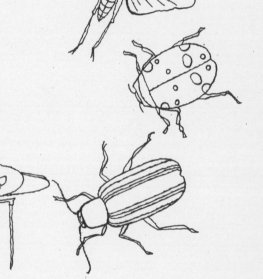

This Little Chick

This little chick ate corn today;
> Hold up thumb.

This little chick ate worms, they say;
> Hold up first finger.

This little chick ate yellow meal;
> Hold up second finger.

This little chick ate potato peel;
> Hold up third finger.

And this little chick, like a fluffy ball,
> Hold up fourth finger.

Ate a teeny, tiny bit of all!
    Corn today! Worms they say! Yellow meal! Potato peel!

● Flannelboard figures needed are five chicks.

- Flannelboard materials needed are ten eggs, a setting hen, and ten baby chickens.

Ten Fluffy Chickens

Five eggs and five eggs,
> Hold up two hands.

That makes ten;

Sitting on top is the Mother Hen.
> Fold one hand over the other.

Crackle, crackle, crackle;
> Clap three times.

What do I see?

Ten fluffy chickens
> Hold up ten fingers.

As yellow as can be!

- Flannelboard figures needed are ten kittens.

Counting Kittens

One kitten with a furry tail;
> Hold up one finger.

Two kittens on the floor;
> Hold up two fingers.

Three kittens in the apple tree;
> Hold up three fingers.

Four kittens at the door;
> Hold up four fingers.

Five kittens roll a yellow ball;
> Hold up five fingers.

Six kittens gently purr;
> Hold up six fingers.

Seven kittens watch a mouse;
> Hold up seven fingers.

Eight kittens wash their fur;
> Hold up eight fingers.

Nine kittens lap their morning milk;
> Hold up nine fingers.

Ten kittens chase a hen.
> Hold up ten fingers.

Help me count the kittens:

1—2—3—4—5!

6—7—8—9—10!
> Bend down fingers one at a time.

Little Kittens

Five little kittens playing on the floor;
> Hold up five fingers.

One smelled a mouse; then there were four.

Four little kittens fat as fat could be;
> Hold up four fingers.

One saw a puppy; then there were three.

Three little kittens watched how birdies flew;
> · Hold up three fingers.

One ran far up the tree; then there were two.

Two little kittens snoozing in the sun;
> Hold up two fingers.

One chased a rabbit; then there was one.

One little kitten looking for some fun;
> Hold up one finger.

He fluffed his tail and scampered off;

Now there isn't even ONE!

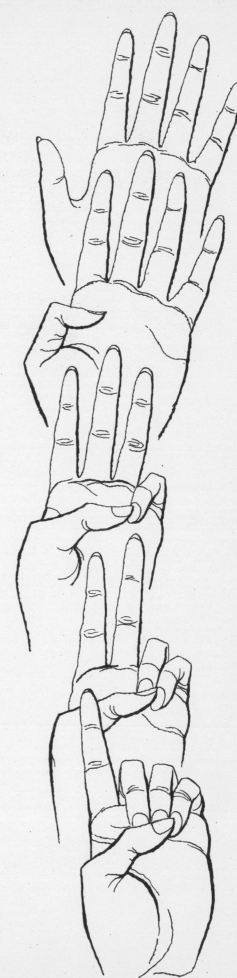

Five Little Pussy Cats

Five little pussy cats;
> Hold up five fingers.

See them play!
> Wiggle fingers.

This one is brown,
> Bend down thumb.

And this one is gray;
> Bend down pointer finger.

This one has a white nose;
> Bend down middle finger.

This one has sharp claws;
> Bend down ring finger.

This one has long whiskers
> Bend down little finger.

And tiny, soft paws.

1, 2, 3, 4, 5 pussy cats,
> Pop up fingers as you count.

Hurry away to scare the mice and rats.
> Wiggle fingers.

SQUEAK!
> Clap hands.

—Adapted

● Flannelboard figures needed
are five kittens.

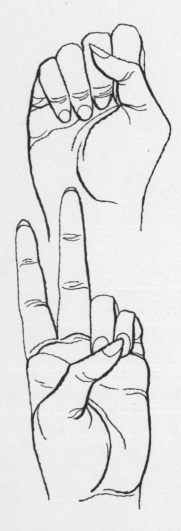

One Little Kitten, One

One little kitten, one
    Hold up one finger.
Said, "Let's have some fun!"
Two little kittens, two
    Hold up two fingers.
Said, "What shall we do?"
Three little kittens, three
    Hold up three fingers.
Said, "Let's climb up that tree."
Four little kittens, four
    Hold up four fingers.
Said, "Let's hide behind the door."
Five little kittens, five
    Hold up five fingers.
Said, "Here's a beehive!"
    Make a fist with other hand.
"Bzzzzzzzzz" went the bee,
And they scampered up a tree!
    Move fingers in running motion.

Kitty and Bunny

Here is a kitty;
    Make a fist with one hand.
Here is a bunny;
    Hold up other hand with pointer and middle fingers up straight.
See his tall ears so pink and funny!
    Wiggle the two extended fingers.
Kitty comes by and licks his face;
    Extend thumb and wiggle near bunny.
And around and around the garden they race;
    Make circular motions with hands.
And then without a single peep,
They both lie down and go to sleep.
    Fold hands.

\Creepy Crawly

Creepy, crawly, creepy, crawly
Goes old Pussy Cat;
> Make fingers creep along opposite arm.

Froggie with a speckled coat
Jumps like that!
> Make leap with arms.

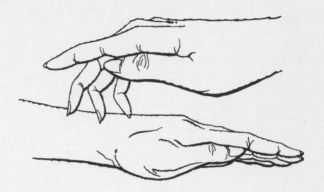

Five Kittens

This kitten said, "I smell a mouse."
> Touch first finger.

This kitten said, "Let's hunt through the house."
> Touch second finger.

This kitten said, "Let's pretend we're asleep."
> Touch third finger.

This kitten said, "Let's go creepity-creep."
> Touch fourth finger.

This kitten said, "Meow, meow.
> Touch thumb.

I saw him run into his hole just now."

—*Maude Burnham*

● Flannelboard figures needed
are five kittens.

Mr. Duck and Mr. Turkey

Mr. Duck went out to walk,
> Hold up thumb.

One day in pleasant weather.
He met Mr. Turkey on the way,
> Hold up other thumb.

And there they walked together.
> Move thumbs together.

"Gobble, gobble, gobble,"
> Move one thumb back and forth.

"Quack, quack, quack."
> Move other thumb back and forth.

"Good-by, good-by,"
> Nod both thumbs.

And then they both walked back.
> Move thumbs apart.

—*Yvonne Altman*

● Flannelboard figures needed
are a duck and a turkey.

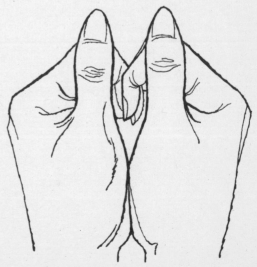

33

Piggies

"It is time for my piggies to go to bed,"
The nice, big, fat Mother Pig said.
"So I will count them first to see
If they have all come back to me.
One little piggie, two little piggies,
> Pop up one finger at a time
> as Mother Pig counts.

Three little piggies dear.
Four little piggies, five little piggies.
Yes, they are all here!
Why, they are the cutest piggies alive.
1, 2, 3, 4, 5!"
> Point to each finger as you count.

—*Maude Burnham*

● Continue the rhyme until all three pigeons are back on the fence. More pigeons may be used to give drill on concepts *four, five,* etc.

Flannelboard materials needed are three pigeons and a felt fence.

Three Little Pigeons

Three little pigeons sitting on a fence;
> Hold up three fingers.

Three little pigeons sitting on a fence;
One flew away!
> Bend down one finger.

Oh, dear, how sad!

Two little pigeons sitting on a fence;
Two little pigeons sitting on a fence;
One flew away!
> Bend down one finger.

Oh, dear, how sad!

One little pigeon sitting on a fence;
One little pigeon sitting on a fence;
He flew away!
> Bend down last finger.

Oh, dear, how sad!

No little pigeons sitting on a fence;
No little pigeons sitting on a fence;
But one came back!
> Hold up one finger.

Hooray!

Once I Saw a Beehive

Once I saw a beehive
> Hump hands together to form hive.

Out in the maple tree.
I said, "Little honeybees,
Come out and play with me!"
"Bzzzzzz!" went the honeybees
Inside the hive;
> Motion of peeking inside hive.

And then they came out—
One, two, three, four, five!
> Show one finger at a time.

● On the flannelboard, place a hive drawn by the children and backed with flannel bits or suede-backed paper. Let the children make the bees also from construction paper.

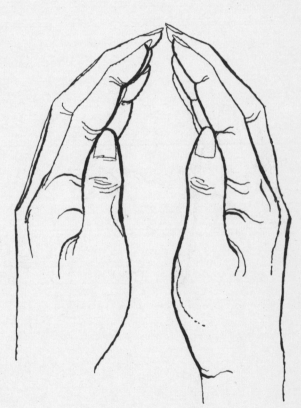

Puppy Jumps Over a Stick

Puppy jumps over the stick;
> Place tips of thumbs together.

Two sticks,
> Place tips of pointer fingers together.

Three,
> Place tips of middle fingers together.

And four;
> Place tips of ring fingers together.

Puppy jumps over a little stick;
> Place tips of little fingers together.

And now there are no more.

- To vary the game, point to fingers as you refer to each puppy.

Flannelboard figures needed are five puppies, a rabbit, a butterfly, and a cat.

Five Little Puppies

Five little puppies were playing in the sun;
> Hold up hands, fingers extended.

This one saw a rabbit, and he began to run;
> Bend down first finger.

This one saw a butterfly, and he began to race;
> Bend down second finger.

This one saw a pussy cat, and he began to chase;
> Bend down third finger.

This one tried to catch his tail, and he went round and round;
> Bend down fourth finger.

This one was so quiet, he never made a sound.
> Bend down thumb.

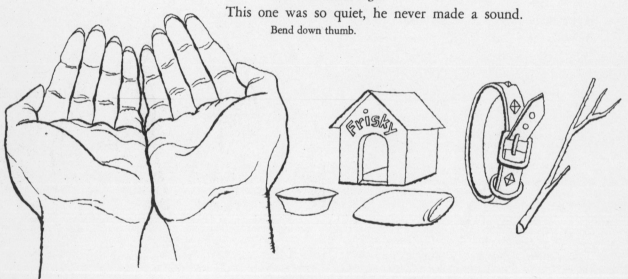

- Flannelboard materials needed are a doghouse, a dog bed, a pan, a dog collar, and a stick.

Frisky's Doghouse

This is Frisky's doghouse;
> Pointer fingers touch to make a roof.

This is Frisky's bed;
> Motion of smoothing.

Here is Frisky's pan of milk
> Cup hands.

So that he can be fed.

Frisky has a collar
> Circle neck with fingers.

With his name upon it, too;

Take a stick and throw it,
> Motion of throwing.

And he'll bring it back to you.
> Clap once.

● Flannelboard figures needed
are ten farmer boys.

Ten Little Farmer Boys

Ten little farmer boys sitting by a vine;
> Hold up hands, fingers extended.

A grasshopper frightened one; then there were nine.
> Bend down one finger.

Nine little farmer boys swinging on a gate;
One turned a somersault; then there were eight.
> Bend down one finger.

Eight little farmer boys counting clouds in heaven;
One of them fell asleep; then there were seven.
> Bend down one finger.

Seven little farmer boys full of monkey tricks;
One tumbled down the hill; then there were six.
> Bend down one finger.

Six little farmer boys went out to find a hive;
A bumblebee stung one; then there were five.
> Bend down one finger.

Five little farmer boys eating more and more;
One got a tummy ache; then there were four.
> Bend down one finger.

Four little farmer boys climbing up a tree;
The rooster chased one away; then there were three.
> Bend down one finger.

Three little farmer boys in overalls blue;
One tumbled off the fence; then there were two.
> Bend down one finger.

Two little farmer boys, both of them named John;
One chased the other; then there was one.
> Bend down one finger.

One little farmer boy hunting for a penny;
He ran to buy some pumpkin seeds; then there weren't any.
> Bend down last finger.

—Adapted from "St. Nicholas Magazine"

FROM OTHER LANDS

Finger rhymes belong to all nations, for they seem to have developed out of the mother-child relationships of the baby's first years. This section includes a number of such plays and action poems from other countries.

The activity is presented first in its native language, then in translation. Children will find great enjoyment in learning the originals.

Les Marionnettes

Ainsi font, font, font
>> Hold up ten fingers and dance them back and forth.

Les petites Marionnettes.

Ainsi font, font, font.
>> Repeat above motions.

Trois petits tours et puis s'en vont.
>> Turn hands three times and hide them behind back.

—Traditional

The Puppets

Ten little puppets
>> Use same actions suggested for the French version above.

Dance in a row.

Three little turns

And away they go.

—Translated by the authors

La Souris

La petite souris a passé par ici.
>> Hold thumb erect and wiggle it.

Celui-ci l'a vue,
>> Shake pointer finger.

Celui-ci a couru après,
>> Shake middle finger.

Celui-ci l'a attrapée,
>> Shake ring finger.

Celui-ci l'a mangée . . . i, i, i.
>> Shake little finger.

—Traditional

The Mouse

A little mouse came out to take a peek.
>> Use same actions suggested for the French version above.

This one saw it.

This one ran after it.

This one caught it.

This one ate it . . . squeak, squeak, squeak.

—Translated by the authors

● Flannelboard materials needed are cards containing the numbers from one to twelve.

J'Irai dans le Bois

Un, deux, trois, j'irai dans le bois,
Quatre, cinq, six, chercher les cerises,
Sept, huit, neuf, dans mon panier neuf,
Dix, onze, douze, elles seront toutes rouges.

—Traditional

To the Woods Goes She

One, two, three, to the woods goes she;
Four, five, six, cherries she picks;
Seven, eight, nine, in her basket fine;
Ten, eleven, twelve, she said,
All the cherries are red, red, red!

—Traditional

Mon Petit Lapin

Mon petit lapin
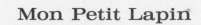
        Hold up two fingers for bunny ears.
A bien du chagrin.
        Extend hands, palms upward.
Il ne saute plus,
        Hands make jumping motion.
Il ne court plus
        Hands make running motion.
Dans le jardin.
Saute, saute, saute, lapin;
        Hands make jumping motions in rhythm to words.
Saute, mon petit lapin.

—Traditional

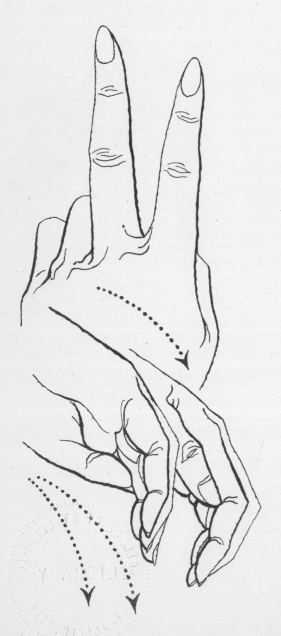

My Little Rabbit

My little rabbit

        Use same actions suggested for the French version above.
Does not have much fun.
He does not jump.
He does not run.
But give him a thump,
And watch him jump.
Jump, little rabbit,
Jump, jump, jump.

—Translated by the authors

Conejito

Conejito que corre,
> Make fingers of hand run up arm and take hold of ear.

Que sube, que te alcanza,
Que te pilla y
Te tira la orejita.

> *—From Chile, Traditional*

Little Rabbit

Run, little rabbit;
> Use same actions suggested for the Spanish version above.

Climb right up here.
He is so hungry
He nibbles at my ear.

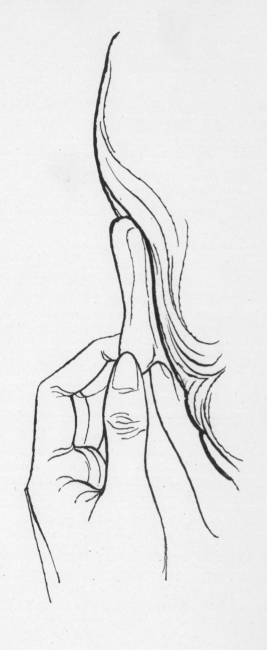

Un Huevito

Éste niñito compró un huevito,
> Hold up thumb.

Éste lo mandó asar,
> Hold up pointer finger.

Éste lo echó sal,
> Hold up middle finger.

Éste lo revolvió
> Hold up ring finger.

Y el más chiquito se lo comió.
> Hold up little finger.

> *—From Chile, Traditional*

An Egg

This little child brought an egg;
> Use same actions suggested for the Spanish version above.

This one put it in a pan;
This one sprinkled on the salt;
This one flipped it in the pan;
Little one said, with a grin,
"I will eat this egg if I can."

> *—Translated by the authors*

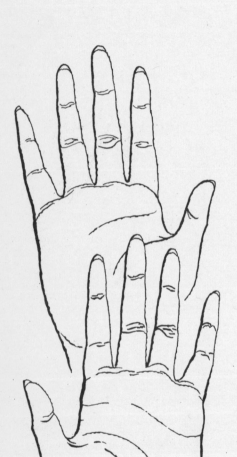

Mi Tío

Mi tío regresó de Chile
y me trajo un abanico.

Hold up one hand.

Mi tío regresó de Peru
y me trajo dos abanicos.

Hold up two hands.

Mi tío regresó de Ecuador
y me trajo tres abanicos.

Tap one foot.

Mi tío regresó de Brazil
y me trajo cuatro abanicos.

Tap both feet.

Mi tío regresó de Uruguay
y me trajo cinco abanicos.

Nod head. Do all actions simultaneously.

—Translated by the authors

My Uncle

My uncle came from Chile
and brought me a fan.

Use same actions suggested for the Spanish version above.

My uncle came from Peru
and brought me two fans.
My uncle came from Ecuador
and brought me three fans.
My uncle came from Brazil
and brought me four fans.
My uncle came from Uruguay
and brought me five fans.

—Traditional

Los Maderos de San Juan

¡Aserrín!
>Pretend to saw wood.

¡Aserrán!
>Continue above action.

Los maderos de San Juan
>Touch pointer finger of left hand with pointer finger of right hand.

Piden queso, piden pan;

Los de Roque,
>Touch middle finger.

Alfandoque;

Los de Rique,
>Touch ring finger.

Alfeñique;

Los de Trique, triquitran.
>Touch little finger.

¡Triqui, triqui, triqui, trán!
>Pretend to saw wood.

¡Triqui, triqui, triqui, trán!

>—*From Colombia, Traditional*

The Woodmen of San Juan

See-saw!

The woodmen work,
>Use same actions suggested for the Spanish version above.

The woodmen of San Juan.

Bread and cheese have they none.

Some ask for cake,

Chocolate cake.

Some ask for pie,

Apple pie.

Some ask for candy, sugar candy.

Handy, spandy, sugar candy!

>—*Translated by the authors*

43

Éste Es un Rey Honrado

Éste es un rey honrado,
>Hold up little finger.

Éste de buen corazón,
>Hold up ring finger.

Éste riquezas tiene,
>Hold up middle finger.

Éste mucho valor,
>Hold up pointer finger.

Y éste es un pícaro ladrón.
>Hold up thumb.

—From Colombia, Traditional

This One Is a Little King

This one is a little king;
>Use same actions suggested for the Spanish version.

This one, a hero true;
This one is rich;
This one is brave;
And this one, my dear, is you.

—Translated by the authors

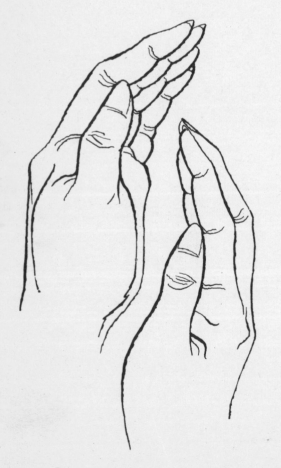

Con las Manos

Con las manos
Aplaudo, aplaudo, aplaudo,
>Clap hands three times.

Y ahora las pongo
En mi regazo.
>Fold hands in lap.

—Translated by Alex Trejo

With the Hands

With my hands
I clap, clap, clap,
>Use same actions suggested
>for the Spanish version above.

And now I lay them
In my lap.

¿Qué Colores Veo?

¡Veo, veo, veo!
¿Qué colores veo?
Ciruelas moradas,
> Point to thumb.

Tomates rojos,
> Point to first finger.

Maíz amarillo,
> Point to second finger.

Patatas cafés,
> Point to third finger.

Lechuga verde,
> Point to fourth finger.

¡Ay que deliciosos!
Todos los colores
Que aprendo al comer.

—Translated by Alex Trejo

● Flannelboard materials needed are purple plums, red tomatoes, yellow corn, brown potatoes, green lettuce.

What Colors Do I See?

See, see, see!
What colors do I see?
Purple plums,
> Use same actions suggested for the Spanish version above.

Red tomatoes,
Yellow corn,
Brown potatoes,
Green lettuce!
Yum, yum, yum, good!
I learn so many colors
When I eat my food!

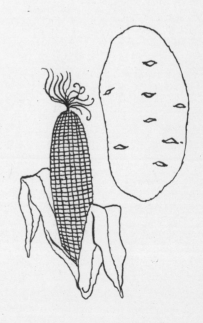

La Mariposa

Uno, dos, tres, cuatro, cinco,
> Pop up fingers on the right hand as you count.

Cogí una mariposa de un brinco.
Seis, siete, ocho, nueve, diez,
> Pop up fingers on the left hand as you count.

La solté brincando otra vez.

—Translated by Alex Trejo

The Butterfly

One, two, three, four, five,
I caught a butterfly.
> Use same actions suggested for the Spanish version above.

Six, seven, eight, nine, ten,
I let him go again.

Italian Lullaby

Bimbo, bimbo, piccolino;
Bello, bello, ditolino.
Quanti, quanti, ce ne sono?
Uno, due, tre,
Quattro, cinque, qui—
Uno, due, tre,
Quattro, cinque.
Batti, batti le manin,
Forte, forte angelin!

—Translated by Harold Lionetti

Italian Lullaby

Baby, baby, little as can be;
Hold your fingers up for me.
How many fingers do we see?
One, two, three, four, five on the left.
One, two, three, four, five on the right.
Clap them now
With all your might!

46

A Japanese Game

Hana, hana, hana, kuchi;
(Nose, nose, nose, mouth;)
Kuchi, kuchi, kuchi, mimi;
(Mouth, mouth, mouth, ear;)
Mimi, mimi, mimi, me;
(Ear, ear, ear, eye.)

—Traditional

● Have children point, using both hands, to nose, mouth, ears, and eyes as each part is mentioned. Maintain a lilting, rhythmic chant.

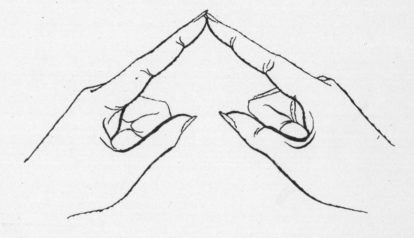

Eins, Zwei

Eins, zwei, Polizei;
    Touch two thumbs together.
Drei, vier, Offizier;
    Touch two pointer fingers together.
Funf, sechs, alte Hex;
    Touch two middle fingers together.
Sieben, acht, gute nacht;
    Touch two ring fingers together.
Neun, zehn, auf wiedersehen.
    Touch two little fingers together.

—Traditional

One, Two

One, two, policemen blue;
    Use same actions suggested for the German version above.
Three, four, captain of the corps;
Five, six, a witch on sticks;
Seven, eight, the hour is late;
Nine, ten, till we meet again.

—Traditional

FUN WITH NUMBERS

Learning is always easier when it can be an enjoyable experience. Learning number concepts should be no exception. Do not use these finger rhymes merely to count the fingers. Remember, you are teaching abstract concepts by encouraging children to visualize these concepts in terms of a certain number of kittens, bunnies, or ducks.

Learning to Count

One, one; now we have begun;
  Hold up one finger.

Two, two; shoes that are new;
  Hold up two fingers.

Three, three; birds in a tree;
  Hold up three fingers.

Four, four; blocks on the floor;
  Hold up four fingers.

Five, five; bees in a hive;
  Hold up five fingers.

Six, six; little drumsticks;
  Hold up six fingers.

Seven, seven; clouds in the heaven;
  Hold up seven fingers.

Eight, eight; cookies on a plate;
  Hold up eight fingers.

Nine, nine; grapes on a vine;
  Hold up nine fingers.

Ten, ten; let's all count again;
  Hold up ten fingers.

1, 2, 3, 4, 5, 6, 7, 8, 9, 10.
  Bend fingers down one by one.

● This poem can be modified into a seatwork activity by giving each child an instruction sheet which asks him to draw two shoes that are new, three birds in a tree, etc.

Flannelboard materials needed are two shoes, three birds, four blocks, five bees, six drumsticks, seven clouds, eight cookies, and nine grapes.

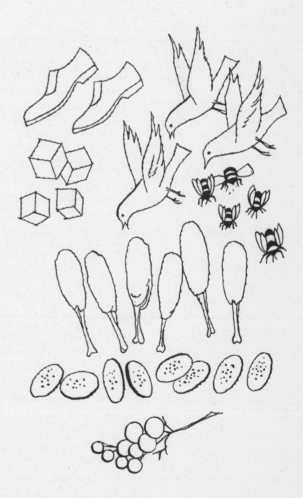

One and Two

One, one. One head
rests on a pillow in a bed.
Palms together, lean head against hands.

Two, two. Two eyes
pretty and blue as the skies.
Point to eyes.

One, one. One nose
smells a lovely, yellow rose.
Point to tip of nose.

Two, two. Two ears
listen for the sounds they'll hear.
Point to ears.

One, one. One chin
open to let our food come in.
Point to chin.

Two, two. Two feet
walk along in shoes so neat.
Point to feet.

Arms, legs, shoulders, neck, toes, hands,
chest grow and grow and grow and grow
as you sleep and rest!
Point to each part of body as it is named.

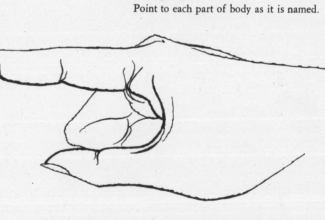

Three Little Nickels

Three little nickels in a pocketbook new;
Hold up three fingers.
One bought a peppermint, and then there were two.
Bend down one finger.
Two little nickels; before the day was done,
One bought an ice-cream cone, and then there was one.
Bend down another finger.
One little nickel; I heard it plainly say,
"I'm going into the piggy bank for a rainy day!"

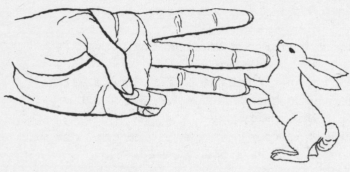

● This poem is good for teaching the recognition of rhyming words. Encourage children to make up their own poems using numbers.

Flannelboard materials needed are three bunnies, three kittens, three frogs, three bears, and three ducks.

I See Three

I see three—one, two, three,

        Hold up three fingers one at a time.

    Three little bunnies

    Reading the funnies.

I see three—one, two, three,

        Bend down three fingers one at a time.

    Three little kittens

    All wearing mittens.

I see three—one, two, three,

        Hold up three fingers one at a time.

    Three little frogs

    Sitting on logs.

I see three—one, two, three,

        Bend down three fingers one at a time.

    Three little bears

    Climbing upstairs.

I see three—one, two, three,

        Hold up three fingers one at a time.

    Three little ducks

    Riding on trucks.

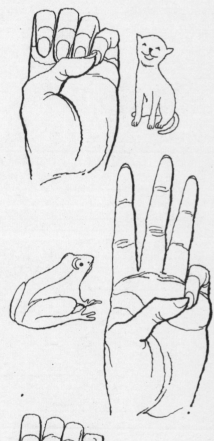

● The number combinations can be placed on the chalkboard or flannelboard when children have reached this stage of learning in their arithmetic.

Honey Bears

This little honey bear was playing peek-a-boo.
  Hold up first finger.
Here is another. Now there are two.
  Hold up second finger.
Two little honey bears said, "Let's climb a tree."
Up came another. Now there are three.
  Hold up third finger.
Three little honey bears said, "I wish there were some more."
Along came another. Now there are four.
  Hold up fourth finger.
Four little honey bears said, "Let's find a beehive."
Here comes another. Now there are five.
  Hold up thumb.
Five little honey bears climbed up that tree.
Two fell down. Now there are three.
  Bend down two fingers.
Three little honey bears said, "Let's climb some more."
Back came another one. Now there are four.
  Hold up fourth finger.
Four little honey bears said, "Let's go to the zoo."
Two of them went. That left just two.
  Bend down two fingers.
Two little honey bears said, "We've had our fun."
They both went home. Now there are none,
  Make fist.

—*Beatrice Bryant*

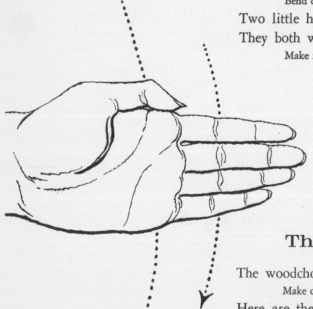

The Woodchopper

The woodchopper chops down an old oak tree;
  Make chopping motion with edge of left hand.
Here are the chips—one, two, and three.
  Count three fingers.
An old lady comes who is looking for sticks;
She picks up the chips—four, five, and six.
  Finish counting by holding up six fingers.

Captain and Men

1, 2, 3, 4, 5 in a row,
> Pop up fingers one at a time on right hand.

A Captain and his men!
And on the other side, you know,
Are 6, 7, 8, 9, and 10.
> Pop up fingers one at a time on left hand.

● Five fishes may be placed on the flannelboard one at a time as the poem is being said. This poem ties in with speech, teaches number concepts, and uses many first-grade reading words. See *Talking Time,* pp. 44, 115, and 126, for speech improvement suggestions involving sounds that occur frequently in this rhyme.

Fred and His Fishes

Fred had a fishbowl.
In it was a fish,
> Hold up one finger.

Swimming around with a swish, swish, swish!
Fred said, "I know what I will do.
I'll buy another and that will make —."
> Children supply number and
> hold up two fingers.

Fred said, "I am sure it would be
Very, very nice if I just had ——."
> Children supply number and hold
> up three fingers.

Fred said, "If I just had one more,
That would make one, two, three, ——."
> Children supply number and
> hold up four fingers.

Fred said, "What fun to see them dive,
One, two, three, four, ——."
> Children supply number and hold
> up five fingers.

How many fishes do you see?
How many fishes? Count them with me!
> Children count to five.

● This is a good action poem which can be used to precede getting children in line to go out to recess. It also can be used to help children "let off steam" on a rainy day.

Flannelboard materials needed are cards with numbers from 1 to 9 printed on them.

One, Two, How Do You Do?

1, 2, how do you do?
1, 2, 3, clap with me;
1, 2, 3, 4, jump on the floor;
1, 2, 3, 4, 5, look bright and alive;
1, 2, 3, 4, 5, 6, your shoe to fix;
1, 2, 3, 4, 5, 6, 7, look up to heaven;
1, 2, 3, 4, 5, 6, 7, 8, draw a round plate;
1, 2, 3, 4, 5, 6, 7, 8, 9, get in line!

Counting Action Rhyme

One, two; sit up. Please do!
    Children sit tall.
Three, four; feet flat on the floor.
    Feet on floor.
Five, six; stir and mix.
    Motion of stirring.
Seven, eight; close the gate.
    Clap.
Nine, ten; make a pen for a hen.
    Interlace fingers.

Rabbits

Ten little rabbits in a row so even;
Hold up both hands, fingers extended.
Three went away. Now there are seven.
Bend down three fingers.
Seven little rabbits eating carrot sticks;
One went away. Now there are six.
Bend down one finger.
Six little rabbits said, "It's getting late."
Two came back. Now there are eight.
Hold up two more fingers.
Eight little rabbits in a rabbit pen;
Two more came along. Now there are ten.
Hold up two more fingers.
Ten little rabbits feeling just fine;
One went to run awhile. Now there are nine.
Bend down one finger.
Nine little rabbits ate all the cake.
One got a tummy ache. Now there are eight.
Bend down one finger.
Eight little rabbits look up to heaven.
One went up there. Now there are seven.
Bend down one finger.
Seven little rabbits with eyes that shine;
Two more joined them. Now there are nine.
Hold up two more fingers.
Nine little rabbits came back again.
Along came another. Now there are ten.
Hold up one more finger.

—*Beatrice Bryant*

● Place the combinations on the chalkboard or flannelboard as each verse is recited. When the children have reached the appropriate stage of learning in arithmetic, have them do some of the problems on the chalkboard.

● This poem can be used as a jump-rope rhyme by substituting the word *skip* for *tap*. In using the poem as a body action rhyme, the leader touches different things in the room as each number is said. A child is chosen to touch the same things in the same order, counting as he does so.

Follow Me

Tap one, tap two,
Be on time whatever you do!
Tap three, tap four,
Will somebody open the door?
Tap five, tap six,
Everybody tap two sticks.
Tap seven, tap eight,
Hurry, now, and don't be late!
Tap nine, tap ten,
I choose (*Name*) to do it again!

—*Olive Amundson*

● Substitute *shirts, pajamas,* or *socks* for *dresses*. Substitute *Daddy* for *Mother*.

See My Clothes

One, two, three, four, five, six, seven, eight, nine;
Hold up nine fingers.
See the dresses on the clothesline;
Some are Mother's and some are mine,
But all of them dry in the yellow sunshine.

● Flannelboard materials needed are these addition cards:

1	2	3	4	5
+1	+2	+3	+4	+5

Arithmetic Problems

One and one are two. That I always knew.
Two and two are four. They could be no more.
Three and three are six—whether books or bricks.
Four and four are eight. I can keep them straight.
Five and five are ten. Write them with a pen.

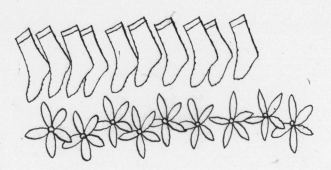

Flannelboard materials needed are ten socks, nine flowers, eight stars, seven boys, six bees, five chickens, four ducks, three kittens, two bunnies, and one puppy. Have the children make the objects and animals themselves.

How Many?

Ten little socks hanging on a line;
Ten fingers extended.
If one blows away, that will leave ——.
Bend down a finger.
Nine little flowers by a garden gate;
I picked a red one, and that leaves ——.
Bend down another finger.
Eight pretty stars shining in the heaven;
A cloud hides one, and now there are ——.
Bend down another finger.
Seven little boys playing with bricks;
One boy runs away, and now there are ——.
Bend down another finger.
Six little bees in a beehive;
One bee flies away, and now there are ——.
Bend down another finger.
Five little chickens by the barn door;
One goes inside, and then there are ——.
Bend down another finger.
Four little ducks in a pond you see;
One duck takes a dive, and so there are ——.
Bend down another finger.
Three little kittens crying, "Mew, mew!
One finds a ball of yarn, and then there are ——.
Bend down another finger.
Two little bunnies hopping in the sun;
One looked for a carrot, and now there is ——.
Bend down another finger.
One little puppy having lots of fun;
He chased a cat, so now there are none.
Place hands behind back.

HOLIDAYS

Holidays always bring excitement and a festive air that calls for special materials to set those days apart.

In this section will be found finger plays and action rhymes for the following holidays. You will find the poems printed in this order:

Hallowe'en

Thanksgiving

Christmas

Hanukkah

Valentine's Day

Easter

Hallowe'en

It was the finest pumpkin that you have ever seen.
> Make circle with arms.

It grew in Tommy's garden on the night of Hallowe'en.
He took his knife to cut the top,
> Action of cutting.

He scooped it with a spoon,
> Action of scooping.

He made two eyes,
> Make round circles with fingers at eyes.

A nose so long,
> Point to nose.

A mouth just like a moon.
> Draw half moon in air.

He put a candle in it,
> Hold up one finger.

Then still as any mouse,
He crept up very slowly to a window in his house.
> Move fingers in creeping motion.

He held the jack o'lantern
> Pretend to hold.

Till his mother cried, "Look here!
It seems to me some brownies
Are hiding very near!"

—Maude Burnham

● Flannelboard materials needed are ten pumpkins.

Ten Little Pumpkins

Ten little pumpkins all in a line;
> Hold up ten fingers.

One became a jack o'lantern,
Then there were nine.
> Bend down one finger.

Nine little pumpkins peeking through the gate;
An old witch took one,
Then there were eight.
> Bend down one finger.

Eight little pumpkins (there never were eleven);
A green goblin took one,
Then there were seven.
> Bend down one finger.

Seven little pumpkins full of jolly tricks;
A white ghost took one,
Then there were six.
> Bend down one finger.

Six little pumpkins glad to be alive;
A black cat took one,
Then there were five.
> Bend down one finger.

Five little pumpkins by the barn door;
A hoot owl took one,
Then there were four.
> Bend down one finger.

Four little pumpkins, as you can plainly see;
One became a pumpkin pie,
Then there were three.
> Bend down one finger.

Three little pumpkins feeling very blue;
One rolled far, far away,
Then there were two.
> Bend down one finger.

Two little pumpkins alone in the sun,
One said, "So long,"
And then there was one.
> Bend down one finger.

One little pumpkin left all alone;
A little boy chose him,
Then there were none.
> Bend down last finger.

Ten little pumpkins in a patch so green
Made everyone happy on Hallowe'en!

Three Little Witches

One little, two little, three little witches
> Hold up fingers one by one.

Ride through the sky on a broom;
> Hands clasped together in front as though grasping broomstick.

One little, two little, three little witches
> Repeat action in line one.

Wink their eyes at the moon.
> Wink one eye while making circle with arms.

● Flannelboard materials needed are three witches on broomsticks and a full moon.

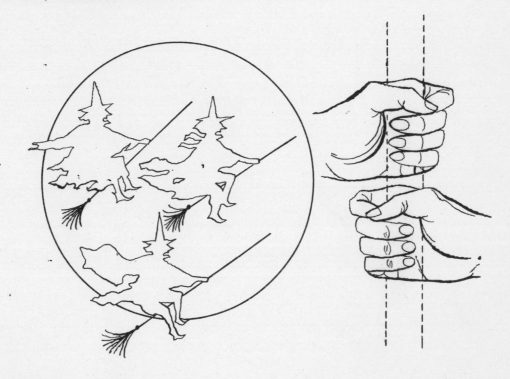

Five Little Goblins

Five little goblins on a Hallowe'en night
Made a very, very spooky sight.
The first one danced on his tippy-tip-toes;
> Hold up first finger.

The next one tumbled and bumped his nose;
> Hold up second finger.

The next one jumped high up in the air;
> Hold up third finger.

The next one walked like a fuzzy bear;
> Hold up fourth finger.

The next one sang a Hallowe'en song.
> Hold up thumb.

Five goblins played the whole night long!

● The word *next* may be changed to *second*, *third*, *fourth*, and *fifth*. Flannelboard materials needed are five goblins.

Thanksgiving

Every day when we eat our dinner,
Our table is very small.
> Show size with two hands.

There's room for Daddy,
> Hold up tall finger.

And Mother,
> Hold up pointer finger.

And Baby, that is all.
> Hold up little finger.

But when Thanksgiving comes,
You can't believe your eyes.
For that same table stretches
> Stretch arms.

Until it is this size!

—*Maude Burnham*

A Thanksgiving Finger Play

Mother, father, sister, brother,
> Point to fingers one at a time.

Baby, too, will pray:
> Place hands together in prayer.

"Thank Thee, Heavenly Father,
On this Thanksgiving Day."

● Flannelboard figures needed
are five Pilgrim children.

Five Little Pilgrims

Five little Pilgrims on Thanksgiving Day:
> Hold up one hand, fingers extended.

The first one said, "I'll have cake if I may."
> Point to thumb.

The second one said, "I'll have turkey roasted."
> Point to pointer finger.

The third one said, "I'll have chestnuts toasted."
> Point to middle finger.

The fourth one said, "I'll have pumpkin pie."
> Point to ring finger.

The fifth one said, "Oh, cranberries I spy."
> Point to little finger.

But before they ate any turkey or dressing,
All of the Pilgrims said a Thanksgiving blessing.
> Touch hands in prayer.

Wake Up, Little Pilgrims

Wake up, little Pilgrims,
The sun's in the East.
> Children sit tall.

Today is the day for our Thanksgiving feast.
> Fold hands.

Come, jump out of bed,
See how tall you can stand.
> Hold up ten fingers.

My, my! But you are a wide-awake band!
> Clap hands.

Wash your hands, wash your faces,
> Motion of washing.

So that you will look neat.
> Fold hands in lap.

Then come to the table; say prayers before you eat.
> Touch hands in prayer.

—*Maude Burnham*

● Have children make up a tune for the words. Dramatize with stick puppets, letting children make their own Indian pictures and gluing them on dowel sticks or tongue depressors.

Ten Little Indians

Ten little Indians dancing in a ring;
> Extend ten fingers and dance them back and forth.

Ten little Indians, hear them sing!
Ooooooooooo—ooooooooooo!
> Give Indian war cry.

Ten little Indians wave tomahawks high;
> Pretend to wave tomahawks above head.

Ten little Indians give their war cry;
Ooooooooooo—ooooooooooo!

Ten little Indians in a teepee;
> Bring finger tips together to make point over head.

Ten little Indians quiet as can be!
> Fold hands.

Sh!
> Finger at lips.

● This poem may be used as a relaxation activity as well as a finger play. To encourage conversation, ask children to pantomime what they want for Christmas and tell about their own dreams for Christmas.

Flannelboard materials needed are five sleeping children, a Christmas tree, Santa Claus, his reindeer and his sleigh, a fireplace hung with stockings, the Christ Child in a manger, miscellaneous presents.

Dreams

Five children dreamed of Christmas day,
     Hold up five fingers.
As fast asleep five children lay.
The first one dreamed of Christmas trees
Trimmed in tinsel gay;
     Bend down thumb.
The second one dreamed of Santa Claus,
His reindeer and his sleigh;
     Bend down pointer finger.
The third one dreamed of a fireplace
And stockings in a row;
     Bend down middle finger.
The fourth one dreamed of the Christ Child
Born so long ago;
     Bend down ring finger.
The fifth one dreamed of presents
Piled beneath a tree.
     Bend down little finger.
You, too, can dream, if you will play
This dreaming game with me.
Let your eyelids gently close,
     Close eyes.
Let your head drop down;
     Relax head.
Let the dreams of Christmas come
As you drift to Sleepy Town.

The Angel on My Christmas Tree

Two small hands that touch in prayer,
> Touch hands as in prayer.

A golden halo in her hair,
> Make circle above head with one hand.

On her back, two silver wings;
> One hand at each shoulder.

Once each year my angel brings
The Christmas story back to me,
While she rests upon my Christmas tree.
> Touch hands again in prayer.

Five Bright Stars

Five bright stars on a Christmas Night,
Wanted to give their very best light.
> Hold up five fingers.

The first one said, "I will shine for the sheep,
And the shepherds who their watch do keep."
> Point to little finger.

The second one said, "I will shine to show
The wise men just which way to go."
> Point to ring finger.

The third one said, "I will shine to see
If folks will remember the prophecy."
> Point to middle finger.

The fourth one said, "I will shine to remind
People on earth to be good and kind."
> Point to pointer finger.

The fifth one, brightest star of all,
Stretched its beams till it reached a stall
> Hands above head.

Where shepherds and wise men knelt to pray
> Hands folded in prayer.

Beside a manger where Jesus lay.
> Extend both hands, palms up.

The STAR OF THE EAST told all the earth
The wonderful news of the Savior's birth.
> Head bowed and hands folded in prayer.

● Flannelboard materials needed are five stars, shepherds, sheep, three wise men, a manger, Mary, Joseph, the Baby Jesus, and assorted animals for the stable.

The Toy Shop

Here is a window in a Christmas Toy Shop;
    Make circle with arms.
This is a round balloon that pops!
    Clap hands.
This is a top that spins in a ring;
    Twirl forefinger.
This is a little bird that can sing;
    Whistle.
This is a soldier that can walk;
    Make two fingers walk.
This is a Ma-ma doll that can talk;
    Ma-ma.
This is a funny jumping-jack man;
    Swing arms out suddenly.
This is a sleepy Raggedy Ann.
    Let arms hang limp; relax head.
And now we will say good-by to the toys,
And tip-toe away without any noise!
    Move fingers in walking motion.

● Flannelboard materials needed are five little pigs.

This Baby Piggie

This baby piggie went to market;
    Hold up thumb.
This baby piggie trimmed the tree;
    Hold up pointer finger.
This baby piggie cooked the dinner,
    Hold up middle finger.
And this baby piggie sang, "Wee, wee!"
    Hold up ring finger.
And this baby piggie cried, "Merry Christmas!"
To everyone he did see.
    Hold up little finger.

● Ten children may be chosen to be the elves to say a line-a-child. Stick puppets or paper sack elves may be made and held up by the children as the poem is said by the group.

Flannelboard materials needed are ten elves, candy canes, a streamlined train, a doll, some chocolate drops, some lollipops, a jack-in-the-box, and some doll socks.

In Santa's Workshop

In Santa's workshop far away,
Ten little elves work night and day.
> Hold up ten fingers.

This little elf makes candy canes;
> Point to little finger on one hand.

This little elf builds streamlined trains;
> Point to ring finger.

This little elf paints dolls for girls;
> Point to middle finger.

This little elf puts in their curls;
> Point to pointer finger.

This little elf dips chocolate drops;
> Point to thumb.

This little elf makes lollipops;
> Point to little finger on other hand.

This little elf packs each jack-in-the-box;
> Point to ring finger.

This little elf sews dolly socks;
> Point to middle finger.

This little elf wraps books for boys;
> Point to pointer finger.

This little elf checks off the toys,
> Point to thumb.

As Santa packs them in his sleigh,
Ready for you on Christmas Day.

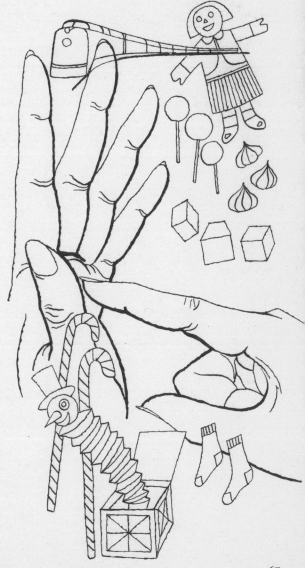

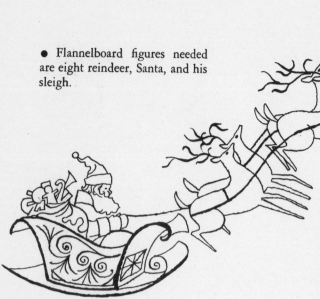

● Flannelboard figures needed are eight reindeer, Santa, and his sleigh.

Eight Tiny Reindeer

Eight tiny reindeer pawing in the snow,
Eight tiny reindeer ready to go;
    Hold up eight fingers.
This one has a shiny red nose;
He tells Santa which way the sleigh goes.
    Point to thumb on one hand.
This one stamps the ice with his hoof;
He wants to hurry to Bobby's roof.
    Point to pointer finger.
This one holds up his antlers high;
At a signal, he will be ready to fly!
    Point to middle finger.
This one makes the sleigh bells ring;
Dishes to Ruthie he wants to bring.
    Point to ring finger.
This one looks all around to see
If there is a dolly for Sarah Lee.
    Point to little finger.
This one stands at attention still
While Santa the sleigh with toys does fill.
    Point to thumb on other hand.
This one pulls at the bit, for he
Wants to start on the long journey.
    Point to pointer finger.
This one, last of the reindeer band,
    Point to middle finger.
Feels the reins pull in Santa's hands.
    Pretend to pull on reins.
With a HI, HI, HO! they are on their way,
And eight tiny reindeer pull the sleigh
To make children happy on Christmas day.

Santa's Reindeer

1, 2, 3, 4, 5 little reindeer
> Pop fingers up one by one.

Stand beside the gate;
"Hurry, Santa," said the five,
"So we will not be late!"
> Make fist.

1, 2, 3, 4, 5 little reindeer;
> Pop fingers up one by one.

Santa said, "Please wait!
Wait for three more little reindeer,
And then that will make eight."
> Hold up three more fingers.

● Ask children if they can remember the names of Santa's reindeer. Extend this activity to a memorization of *A Visit From St. Nicholas* by Clement Moore.

Flannelboard materials needed are eight reindeer and Santa.

Christmas Presents

See all the presents by the Christmas tree;
Some for you
> Point to neighbor.

And some for me;
> Point to self.

Long ones,
> Show width with two hands spread apart.

Tall ones,
> Measure with hand from floor.

Short ones, too;
> Measure shortness.

And here is a round one
> Make circle with arms.

Wrapped in blue.
Isn't it fun to look and see
All of the presents by the Christmas tree?
> Point hands to shape tree.

● This poem brings in four concepts: long, short, tall, round.

Flannelboard materials needed are gaily wrapped Christmas presents, all shapes and sizes. Be sure to include a round one wrapped in blue.

This Little Present

This little present goes to Mary;
Bend down the ring finger.
This little present goes to Ned;
Bend down the middle finger.
This little present goes to Harry;
Bend down the pointer finger.
And this little present goes to Ted;
Bend down the thumb.
This little present cried, "Boo-hoo-hoo!
Wiggle little finger.
Please put me into the Christmas stocking, too!"

—Adapted

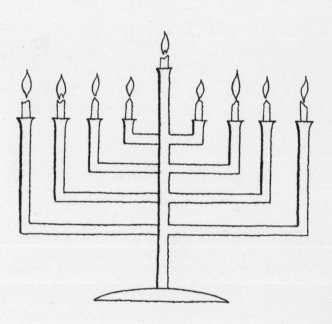

Hanukkah Lights

One light, two lights, three lights, and four,
Hold up four fingers, one at a time.
Five lights, six lights, and three more;
Hold up five more fingers.
Twinkle, twinkle, nine pretty lights
Move fingers.
In a golden Menorah bright!
Cup palms of hands.

For My Friends

To every little friend of mine,
I'll send a pretty valentine.
> Make heart shape with thumbs and forefingers.

This one is like a little book;
> Close palms together.

You'll find a message, if you'll look.
> Open palms.

I'll use an envelope for this.
> Two fists together.

I'll write my name, then seal a kiss.
> One hand closes on fingers of other hand.

What color shall I give to you?
Orange, purple, green, or blue?
Yellow or pink? White or red?
Or maybe a lacy one instead.

—Adapted from Maude Burnham

How Many Valentines?

Valentines, valentines;
How many do you see?
Valentines, valentines;
Count them with me:
   One for Father,
   > Hold up thumb.

   One for Mother,
   > Hold up pointer finger.

   One for Grandma, too;
   > Hold up middle finger.

   One for Sister,
   > Hold up ring finger.

   One for Brother,
   > Hold up little finger.

And here is one for YOU!
> Make heart shape with thumbs and pointer fingers.

● Flannelboard figures needed are six heart-shaped, red felt valentines.

● Flannelboard figures needed
are five heart-shaped, red felt
valentines.

Valentines

Five gay valentines
> Hold up five fingers.

From the ten-cent store;
I sent one to Mother,
> Bend down a finger.

Now there are four.

Four gay valentines,
Pretty ones to see;
I give one to Brother,
> Bend down a finger.

Now there are three.

Three gay valentines,
Yellow, red, and blue;
I give one to Sister,
> Bend down a finger.

Now there are two.

Two gay valentines,
My, we have fun;
I give one to Daddy,
> Bend down a finger.

Now there is one.

One gay valentine,
The story is almost done;
I give it to Baby,
> Bend down last finger.

Now there are none.

—Beatrice Bryant

● Flannelboard figures needed
are five heart-shaped, red felt
valentines.

Five Little Valentines

One little valentine said, "I love you."
> Hold up fist; extend one finger.

Tommy made another; then there were two.
> Extend another finger.

Two little valentines, one for me;
Mary made another; then there were three.
> Extend another finger.

Three little valentines said, "We need one more."
Johnny made another; then there were four.
> Extend another finger.

Four little valentines, one more to arrive;
Susan made another; then there were five.
> Extend another finger.

Five little valentines all ready to say,
"Be my valentine on this happy day."

On Easter Day

On Easter Day, we go to church.
> Place two fists together.

The bell rings from the steeple;
> Extend two pointer fingers
> to make steeple.

When the doors are open wide,
> Interlock fingers and turn hands
> so that fingers stand up.

Inside you'll see all the people.

Five Little Easter Eggs

Five little Easter eggs lovely colors wore;
> Hold up five fingers.

Mother ate the blue one, then there were four.
> Bend down one finger.

Four little Easter eggs, two and two, you see;
Daddy ate the red one, then there were three.
> Bend down one finger.

Three little Easter eggs; before I knew,
Sister ate the yellow one, then there were two.
> Bend down one finger.

Two little Easter eggs, oh, what fun!
Brother ate the purple one, then there was one.
> Bend down one finger.

One little Easter egg; see me run!
I ate the very last one, and then there were none.
> Bend down last finger.

● This poem is good for teaching color concepts.

Flannelboard figures needed are five Easter eggs, one blue, one red, one yellow, one purple, and one green.

Easter Rabbits

Five little Easter rabbits
Hold up five fingers.
Sitting by the door;
One hopped away, and then there were four.
Bend down one finger.

Refrain

Hop, hop, hop, hop;
Clap on each hop.
See how they run!
Hop, hop, hop, hop!
Clap on each hop.
They think it great fun!
Four little Easter rabbits
Hold up four fingers.
Under a tree;
One hopped away, and then there were three.
Bend down one finger.

Repeat refrain

Three little Easter rabbits
Hold up three fingers.
Looking at you;
One hopped away, and then there were two.
Bend down one finger.

Repeat refrain

Two little Easter rabbits
Hold up two fingers.
Resting in the sun;
One hopped away, and then there was one.
Bend down one finger.

Repeat refrain

One little Easter rabbit
Left all alone;
He hopped away, and then there were none.
Hand behind back.

Refrain

Hop, hop, hop, hop!
Clap on each hop.
All gone away!
Hop, hop, hop, hop!
Clap on each hop.
They'll come back some day.

—Unknown

The Rabbits

A family of rabbits lived under a tree;
> Close right hand and hide it under left arm.

A father, a mother, and babies three.
> Hold up thumb, then fingers in succession.

Sometimes the bunnies would sleep all day;
> Make fist.

But when night came, they liked to play.
> Wiggle fingers.

Out of the hole they'd go creep, creep, creep,
> Move fingers in creeping motion.

While the birds in the trees were all asleep.
> Rest face on hands, place palms together.

Then the bunnies would scamper about and run . . .
> Wiggle fingers.

Uphill, downhill! Oh, what fun!
> Move fingers vigorously.

But when the mother said, "It's time to rest,"
> Hold up middle finger.

Pop! They would hurry
> Clap hands after "Pop!"

Right back to their nest!
> Hide hand under arm.

● Flannelboard materials needed are a family of rabbits, a round black felt piece for a "hole," and a green felt hill. Have children dramatize the selection by moving the figures on the flannelboard as the group says the rhyme.

Twelve Little Rabbits

Twelve little rabbits in a rabbit pen;
Two hopped away and then there were ten.
> Hold up ten fingers.

Ten little rabbits with ears up straight;
Two hopped away and then there were eight.
> Bend down two fingers.

Eight little rabbits doing funny tricks;
Two hopped away and then there were six.
> Bend down two fingers.

Six little rabbits eating carrots from the store;
Two hopped away and then there were four.
> Bend down two fingers.

Four little rabbits looked for gardens new;
Two hopped away and then there were two.
> Bend down two fingers.

Two little rabbits found a new friend;
They hopped away, and that is the end.
> Bend down last two fingers.

● Flannelboard figures needed are twelve rabbits.

This Little Bunny

This little bunny has two pink eyes;
Bend down first finger.
This little bunny is very wise;
Bend down second finger.
This little bunny is soft as silk;
Bend down third finger.
This little bunny is white as milk;
Bend down fourth finger.
This little bunny nibbles away
Bend down thumb.
At cabbages and carrots the live-long day!

● Flannelboard figures needed are five rabbits.

Five Little Rabbits

Five little rabbits under a log;
Hold up fingers of one hand.
This one said, "Sh! I hear a dog!"
Point to first finger.
This one said, "I see a man!"
Point to second finger.
This one said, "Run while you can!"
Point to third finger.
This one said, "I'm not afraid!"
Point to fourth finger.
This one said, "Let's hide in the shade!"
Point to thumb.
A man and his dog went hurrying by,
And you should have seen those rabbits fly!

Once There Was a Bunny

Once there was a bunny
Double left fist and extend two fingers for ears.
And a green, green cabbage head;
Double fist on right hand.
"I think I'll have some breakfast," the little bunny said;
Move bunny toward cabbage head.
So he nibbled and he nibbled,
Move fingers on left hand.
Then he turned around to say,
"I think this is the time I should be hopping on my way!"
Make hopping movements with left hand.

—*Traditional*

HOME AND FAMILY

Home and family life are important aspects of the social studies program in kindergarten and the primary grades. The finger plays in this section will supplement that program by providing oral language and dramatic play experiences for children.

My Family

Here is my pretty mother;
Point to pointer finger.
Here is my father tall;
Point to middle finger.
Here is my older brother,
Point to ring finger.
And that isn't all;
Here is my baby brother,
Point to little finger.
As small as small can be;
Who is this other person?
Point to thumb.
Why, of course, it's ME!
1, 2, 3, 4, 5, you see,
Touch each finger as you count.
Make a very nice family!

See My Family

See my family! See them all!
Hold up five fingers.
Some are short,
Hold up thumb.
And some are tall.
Hold up middle finger.
Let's shake hands. "How do you do?"
Clasp hands and shake.
See them bow. "How are you?"
Bend fingers.
Father,
Hold up middle finger.
Mother,
Hold up pointer finger.
Sister,
Hold up ring finger.
Brother,
Hold up thumb.
And me;
Hold up little finger.
All polite to one another.

This Is the Father

This is the father who brings us our bread;
Point to middle finger.
This is the mother who puts us to bed;
Point to pointer finger.
This is the brother who plays with his ball;
Point to ring finger.
This is the sister who plays with her doll;
Point to thumb.
And this is the baby, the smallest of all.
Point to little finger.

—*Maude Burnham*

Here Is Baby's Tousled Head

Here is Baby's tousled head;
> Make a fist.

He nods and nods;
> Bend fist back and forth.

Let's put him to bed.
> Bend other arm and tuck fist into crook of elbow.

—Unknown

Five Little Babies

Five little babies say, "Goodnight."
> Show fist.

Five little babies say, "Sleep tight."
> Hold up five fingers.

Five little babies go to sleep,
And lie very still without a peep.
First is the little one.
Down he goes,
> Bend down little finger.

Down he goes on his little red nose.
The second one says, "I'm tired, too.
Do you mind if I lie down near you?"
> Bend down ring finger.

Then comes the third, the tallest one.
> Bend down middle finger.

He likes to sleep. It's lots of fun!
Down he goes and that makes three
Sleeping so very quietly.
Now let's look at the other two.
Tall one,
> Bend down pointer finger.

Small one,
> Bend down thumb.

What do they do?
They follow you, for you are the best.
> Point to neighbor.

So close your eyes. It is time to rest.

—Maude Burnham

● This poem can be used as a relaxation activity.

This Little Boy

This little boy is just going to bed.
Down on the pillow he lays his head,
Palms together at side of face.
Wraps himself up in his blankets tight,
Hands folded across chest.
And this is the way he sleeps all night.
Morning comes. He opens his eyes.
Children sit up tall.
Back with a toss the covers fly.
Spread arms apart quickly.
Soon he is up and dressed for play,
Ready for school and a bright new day.

—Maude Burnham

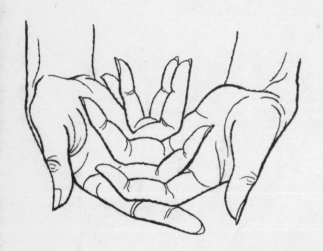

Here Are Mother's Knives and Forks

Here are Mother's knives and forks;
Interlock fingers, palms up.
This is Father's table;
Fingers interlocked, palms down.
This is Sister's looking glass,
Make peak of two pointer fingers.
And this is Baby's cradle.
Interlock fingers and rock back and forth;
thumbs and little fingers should be extended.

—Traditional

Thee Thee That

Grandmother Thee Thee That
Pats one foot, like that;
      Pat one foot.
Grandmother Thee Thee That
Pats two feet, like that;
      Pat both feet.
Grandmother Thee Thee That
Pats one hand, like that;
      Pat one hand.
Grandmother Thee Thee That
Pats two hands, like that;
      Clap hands together silently.
Grandmother Thee Thee That
Nods her head, like that;
      Nod head several times.
Funny old Grandmother
  Thee Thee That.

—Robert West, Lou Kenedy, and Anna Carr

● The game can be continued having children pat their heads, cheeks, chins, elbows, knees, shoulders, and noses.

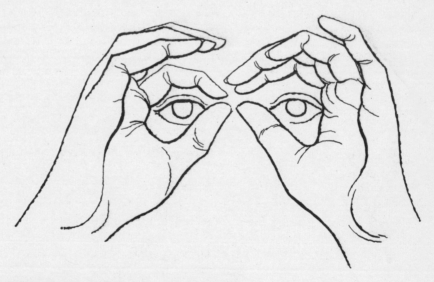

These Are Grandmother's Glasses

These are Grandmother's glasses;
      Make circles around each eye with fingers.
This is Grandmother's cap;
      Hold fingers interlocked over head.
This is the way she folds her hands,
      Fold hands.
And lays them in her lap.
      Lay hands in lap.

—Traditional

Indian Finger Game

This belongs to Father;
> Hold up thumb.

This belongs to Mother;
> Hold up pointer finger.

This belongs to Sister;
> Hold up middle finger.

This belongs to Brother;
> Hold up ring finger.

And this belongs, if you would know,
To Grandfather; we love him so.
> Hold up little finger.

Then a little bird, you understand,
Builds a nest in the palm of your hand;
> Cup hand.

And then the birdies fly away;
> Flutter fingers.

We'll follow to see where they stay.
> Make fingers go up opposite arm.

Follow, follow, follow, follow;
Here they are up in the hollow!
> Place fist under opposite arm.

—Traditional

● Flannelboard figures needed are a washboard, a tub, a cake of soap, a yarn clothesline, and articles of clothing for the clothesline.

Here's a Little Washboard

Here's a little washboard;
> Two hands together, fingertips pointed down.

Here's a little tub;
> Make circle with arms.

Here's a little cake of soap,
> Make circle with two hands.

And here's the way we scrub;
> Motion of rubbing.

Here's a line away up high;
> Middle fingers touching.

Now the clothes are drying;
> Hold up palms.

Hear the wind come whistling by;
> Wave arms.

See! The clothes are flying.
> Make swinging motion with arms.

—Unknown

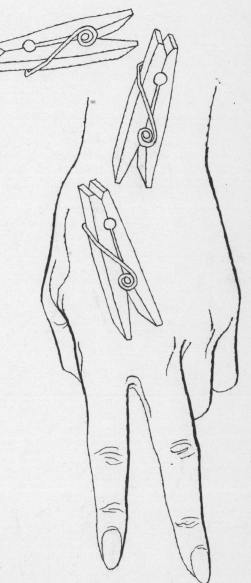

● For the flannelboard, use real clothespins. Paste a strip of felt or sandpaper on each to make it adhere to the board.

Ten Little Clothespins

Ten little clothespins hanging on a line;
> Hold up ten fingers.

One lost his grip and then there were nine.
> Bend down a finger.

Nine little clothespins standing up so straight;
One broke his spring and then there were eight.
> Bend down a finger.

Eight little clothespins in a line so even;
One went snip-snap and then there were seven.
> Bend down a finger.

Seven little clothespins; (Are you keeping score?)
Three took flip-flops and then there were four.
> Bend down three fingers.

Four little clothespins joyful as could be;
One opened his mouth and then there were three.
> Bend down a finger.

Three little clothespins with nothing left to do;
One turned a somersault and then there were two.
> Bend down a finger.

Two little clothespins smiling at the sun;
One felt a raindrop and then there was one.
> Bend down a finger.

One little clothespin left all alone to say,
"This is the end of the line. I'll see you next washday!"

—Mildred Coiner

● This action poem can be sung to the tune of "Here We Go Round The Mulberry Bush." Any other month can be substituted for September.

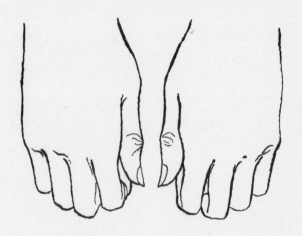

This Is the Way

This is the way we wash our clothes
  On a bright September morning;
    Motion of washing.
This is the way we dry our clothes
  On a bright September morning;
    Motion of hanging clothes on line.
This is the way we sprinkle our clothes
  On a bright September morning;
    Motion of sprinkling.
This is the way we iron our clothes
  On a bright September morning;
    Motion of ironing.
This is the way we fold our clothes
  On a bright September morning;
    Motion of folding.
This is the way we hang up our clothes
  On a bright September morning;
    Motion of hanging up clothes.
This is the way we wear our clothes
  On a bright September morning.
    Indicate articles of clothing.
Monday, wash! Tuesday, dry!
Wednesday, sprinkle! Thursday, iron!
Friday, fold! Saturday, hang up! Sunday, wear!

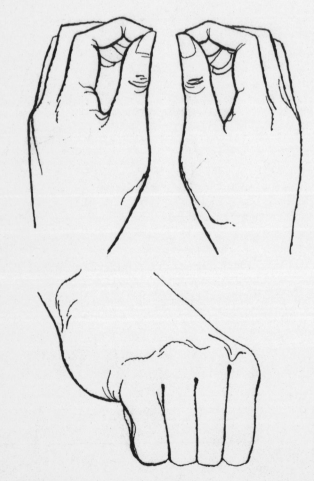

This Is a Fence

This is a fence around the yard;
> Hold up ten fingers.

Here is a house for my family;
> Hands form a roof.

Here is a church where we all go;
> Pointer fingers point for a steeple.

And here is a bed for me, me, me!
> Lace fingers and rock them back and forth.

Here's a Cup of Tea

Here's a cup, and here's a cup,
> Make fist of left hand, then right hand.

And here's a pot of tea;
> Add spout to right hand by protruding thumb.

Pour a cup, and pour a cup,
> Pour into left and then right.

And have a cup with me!
> Extend cup to neighbor and pretend to be drinking.

—Traditional

Two Little Houses

Two little houses closed up tight;
> Two closed fists.

Open up the windows and let in the light.
> Spread hands apart.

Ten little people tall and straight,
> Hold up ten fingers.

Ready for the bus at half past eight!
> Fingers make running motion.

—Unknown

● *Bus* can be changed to *school* or *church*.

Someone Is Knocking

Someone is knocking, one, two, three;
Give three knocks.

Someone is knocking. Who can it be?

Who has come to call upon me?
Motion of opening door.

Why, good morning, Mrs. Brown;
Motion of shaking hands.

I didn't know that you were in town!

What a lovely, lovely gown!
Hands spread apart.

Here's a chair. Won't you sit down?
Indicate a chair.

I'm glad you came to call upon me;

Will you have a cup of tea?
Extend one cupped hand.

Houses

Here is a nest for the robin;
Cup both hands.

Here is a hive for the bee;
Fists together.

Here is a hole for the bunny;
Finger and thumb make a circle.

And here is a house for ME!
Fingertips together to make a roof.

—*Unknown*

IN FIELDS AND WOODS

In fields and woods there is enchantment, for that is where fairies and brownies dwell. But there, too, are found real-life creatures like frogs, ants, squirrels, and owls that can hold more interest than wee folk from fairyland.

Finger plays provide an excellent medium for introducing children to the animals, birds, and insects that they will encounter in their immediate surroundings.

● Flannelboard figures needed are a rabbit, a dog, an elephant, a frog, a goldfish, and a bird.

What the Animals Do

We'll hop, hop, hop like a bunny,
Make hopping motion with hand.
And run, run, run like a dog;
Make running motion with fingers.
We'll walk, walk, walk like an elephant,
Make walking motion with arms.
And jump, jump, jump like a frog;
Make jumping motions with arms.
We'll swim, swim, swim like a goldfish,
Make swimming motion with hand.
And fly, fly, fly like a bird;
Make flying motion with arms.
We'll sit right down and fold our hands,
Fold hands in lap.
And not say a single word!

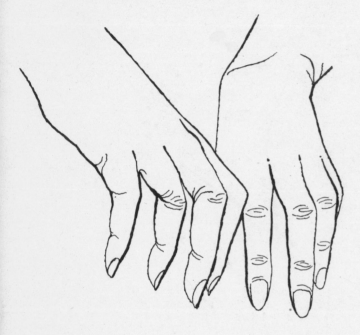

● Flannelboard figures needed are five squirrels.

Five Little Squirrels

Five little squirrels sat up in a tree;
Hold up five fingers.
This little squirrel said, "What do I see?"
Point to thumb.
This little squirrel said, "I smell a gun!"
Point to pointer finger.
This little squirrel said, "Oh, let's run!"
Point to middle finger.
This little squirrel said, "Let's hide in the shade."
Point to ring finger.
This little squirrel said, "I'm not afraid."
Point to little finger.
Then BANG went the gun!
Clap hands.
And away the little squirrels ran, every one.
Make running motions with fingers.

—Traditional

Squirrel in a Tree

This is the squirrel that lives in a tree;
>Make fist; hold two fingers erect.

This is the tree which he climbs;
>Motion of fingers climbing up opposite arm.

This is the nut that he takes from me;
>Make small circle.

As I sit very still sometimes.
>Fold hands.

● Flannelboard materials needed are a squirrel, a tree, and a nut.

Five Little Mice

Five little mice on the pantry floor;
>Hold up five fingers.

This little mouse peeked behind the door;
>Bend down little finger.

This little mouse nibbled at the cake;
>Bend down ring finger.

This little mouse not a sound did make;
>Bend down middle finger.

This little mouse took a bite of cheese;
>Bend down pointer finger.

This little mouse heard the kitten sneeze.
>Bend down thumb.

"Ah-choo!" sneezed kitten, and "Squeak!" they cried,
As they found a hole and ran inside.
>Make running motion with fingers
>and hide hands behind back.

● Flannelboard figures needed are five mice.

Where Are the Baby Mice?

Where are the baby mice?
Squeak, squeak, squeak!
>Make fist and hide it behind you.

I cannot see them;
Peek, peek, peek!
>Show fist and extend it.

Here they come out of their hole in the wall.
One, two, three, four, five, and that is all!
>Show one finger at a time.

● Put felt mice on the flannelboard one at a time.

● Flannelboard materials needed are ten grasshoppers.

Ten Little Grasshoppers

Ten little grasshoppers swinging on a vine;
> Hold up hands, fingers extended.

One ate too many berries and then there were nine.
> Bend down one finger.

Nine little grasshoppers sitting on the gate;
One was blown away and then there were eight.
> Bend down one finger.

Eight little grasshoppers flying toward heaven;
One got lost upon a cloud and then there were seven.
> Bend down one finger.

Seven little grasshoppers lived between two bricks;
One said, "I'll hop away," and then there were six.
> Bend down one finger.

Six little grasshoppers glad to be alive;
One chased a bumblebee and then there were five.
> Bend down one finger.

Five little grasshoppers jumping on the floor;
One hid inside a crack and then there were four.
> Bend down one finger.

Four little grasshoppers saw a tiny flea;
One tried to chase it and then there were three.
> Bend down one finger.

Three little grasshoppers, and what did they do?
One skipped merrily away and then there were two.
> Bend down one finger.

Two little grasshoppers dancing in the sun;
One hid behind a tree and then there was one.
> Bend down one finger.

One little grasshopper, left all alone,
Hopped over the grass and then there were none.
> Make fist.

Eency Weency Spider

The eency weency spider
Went up the water spout;
Fingers imitate a moving spider.
Down came the rain and
Fingers imitate falling rain.
Washed the spider out;
Out came the sun and
Arms make large circle.
Dried up all the rain;
And the eency weency spider
Went up the spout again.
Fingers imitate a moving spider.

—*Traditional*

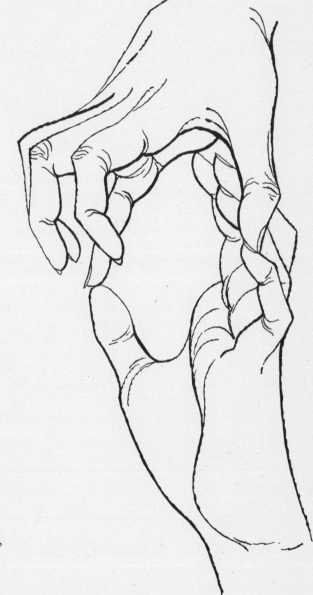

Sleepy Caterpillars

"Let's go to sleep," the little caterpillars said,
Bend ten fingers into palms.
As they tucked themselves into their beds.
They will awaken by and by,
Slowly unfold and hold up fingers.
And each one will be a lovely butterfly!
Hands make flying motion.

• Substitute goldfish, froggie, turtle.

Dive, Little Tadpole

Dive, little tadpole, one;
  Hold up one finger.
Dive, little tadpoles, two;
  Hold up two fingers.
Swim, little tadpoles, Oh, oh, oh!
  Clap three times.
Or I will catch YOU!
  Point.

• Flannelboard figures needed are ten frogs.

Ten Little Froggies

Ten little froggies were swimming in a pool;
  Hold up ten fingers.
This little froggie said, "Let's go to school!"
  Point to thumb.
This little froggie said, "Oh, yes! Let's go!"
  Point to pointer finger.
This little froggie said, "We'll sit in a row."
  Point to middle finger.
This little froggie said, "We'll learn to read."
  Point to ring finger.
This little froggie said, "Yes, yes, indeed."
  Point to little finger.
This little froggie said, "We'll learn to write."
  Point to other thumb.
This little froggie said, "We'll try with all our might."
  Point to pointer finger.
This little froggie said, "We will draw and sing."
  Point to middle finger.
This little froggie said, "We'll learn EVERYTHING!"
  Point to ring finger.
This little froggie said, "Then after school,
  Point to little finger.
We'll come back here and swim in our pool."

Things that Hop

Here is a froggie, hippety-hop;
    Make arms leap forward.
With a hop,
    One big hop.
And a stop,
And a hop,
    Another big hop.
And a stop!

● Substitute grasshopper, cricket, or rabbit.

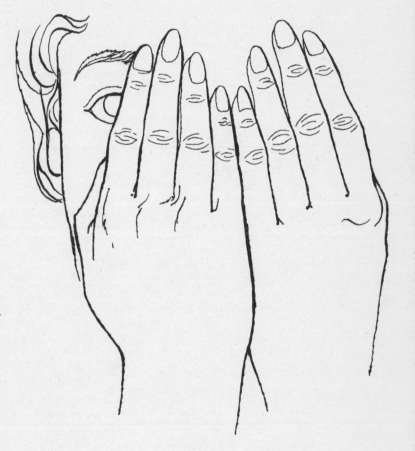

I Am a Little Toad

I am a little toad,
Hopping down the road.
    Make fingers hop in time to verses.
Just listen to my song;
I sleep all winter long;
    Palms together at side of head.
When spring comes, I peep out,
    Peep behind hands.
And then I jump about;
    Make arms jump.
And now I catch a fly,
    Clap hands.
And now I wink my eye;
    Wink one eye.
And now and then I hop,
    Make hands hop.
And now and then I stop!
    Fold hands.

    —*Old Rhyme*

93

● Flannelboard figures needed are five turtles.

Turtles

One little turtle feeling so blue;
>Hold up one finger.

Along came another. Now there are two.
>Hold up two fingers.

Two little turtles on their way to tea;
Along came another. Now there are three.
>Hold up three fingers.

Three little turtles going to the store;
Along came another. Now there are four.
>Hold up four fingers.

Four little turtles going for a drive;
Along came another. Now there are five.
>Hold up five fingers.

—*Beatrice Bryant*

Five Little Seashells

Five little seashells lying on the shore;
>Hold up five fingers.

Swish! went the waves, and then there were four.
>Bend down one finger.

Four little seashells cozy as could be;
Swish! went the waves, and then there were three.
>Bend down one finger.

Three little seashells all pearly new;
Swish! went the waves, and then there were two.
>Bend down one finger.

Two little seashells sleeping in the sun;
Swish! went the waves, and then there was one.
>Bend down one finger.

One little seashell left all alone
Whispered "Shhhhhhhh" as I took it home.
>Bend down last finger.

Five Little Robins

Five little robins in a sycamore tree,
A father,
> Hold up thumb.

A mother,
> Hold up pointer finger.

And babies three;
> Hold up remaining fingers.

Father brought a worm,
> Point to thumb.

Mother brought a bug;
> Point to pointer finger.

The three baby robins started to tug;
This one ate the bug,
> Point to middle finger.

This one ate the worm,
> Point to ring finger.

And this one sat and waited for his turn.
> Point to little finger.

Little Birds

One little bird with lovely feathers blue
> Hold up first finger.

Sat beside another one. Then there were two.
> Hold up second finger.

Two little birds singing in the tree;
Another came to join them. Then there were three.
> Hold up third finger.

Three little birds wishing there were more;
Along came another bird. Then there were four.
> Hold up fourth finger.

Four little birds glad to be alive
Found a lonely friend. Then there were five.
> Hold up thumb.

Five little birds just as happy as can be;
Five little birds singing songs for you and me.

—Betty McAllister

● Flannelboard figures needed
are five birds.

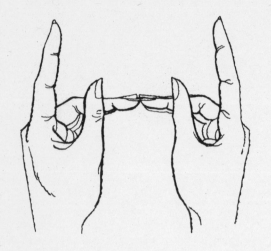

Swinging Birds

Two tall telephone poles,
> Hold up hands, palms inward, pointer fingers erect.

Across them a wire is strung;
> Extend middle fingers until they touch at tips.

Two little birds hopped on,
> Move thumbs to touch extended middle fingers.

And swung and swung and swung.
> Swing hands back and forth.

—Traditional

Here Is a Bunny

Here is a bunny with ears so funny;
> Two fingers up straight.

Here is his hole in the ground;
> Make circle of forefinger and thumb.

Up go his ears and he runs to his hole,
> Motion of running fingers.

When he hears a strange little sound.
> Clap hands.

—Traditional

Striped Chipmunk

A little striped chipmunk
Sat up in a tree,
> Make fist and protrude thumb.

Counting all his chestnuts,
One, two, and three.
> Point to three fingers.

When little Betty Boston went out to play,
The chipmunk flipped his tail,
And ran far, far away!
> Hide hand behind back.

—Adapted from Maude Burnham

Five Little Busy Bees

Five little busy bees on a day so sunny;
> Hold up one hand, fingers extended.

Number one said, "I'd like to make some honey."
> Bend down first finger.

Number two said, "Tell me, where shall it be?"
> Bend down second finger.

Number three said, "In the old honey-tree."
> Bend down third finger.

Number four said, "Let's gather pollen sweet."
> Bend down fourth finger.

Number five said, "Let's take it on our feet."
> Bend down thumb.

So the five little bees went buzzing along,
Humming their busy little honey-bee song.
ZZZZZZZZZZZZZZZZZZZZZZZZ!

● This poem will be helpful to children having trouble with the "z" sound. See *Talking Time,* page 47, for ideas and instructions.

Flannelboard figures needed are five bees.

Counting Tumbleweeds

Ten little tumbleweeds by the corral gate;
> Hold up both hands, fingers extended.

The wind whooshed two away, and then there were eight.
> Bend down two fingers.

Eight little tumbleweeds said, "Oh, fiddlesticks!
We may as well dance with the wind." Then there were six.
> Bend down two fingers.

Six little tumbleweeds went out to explore;
Along came a whirlwind, and then there were four.
> Bend down two fingers.

Four little tumbleweeds admiring the view;
Then there came a gentle breeze; so there were two.
> Bend down two fingers.

Two little tumbleweeds; round and round they spun
Until they were out of sight; then there were none!
> Make fist.

MAKE BELIEVE

Perhaps more of the finger plays in this book should be included under this section, since many require an active imagination. However, this section has been reserved for those wee folk who inhabit fairyland — fairies, brownies, elves, and other pixies.

Tall and Small

Here is a giant who is tall, tall, tall;
> Children stand up tall.

Here is an elf who is small, small, small;
> Children slowly sink to floor.

The elf who is small will try, try, try
> Children slowly rise.

To reach to the giant who is high, high, high.
> Children stand tall, stretch, and reach arms high.

—Unknown

The Elf's Coat

Under a toadstool, there sat a wee elf;
He rocked to and fro and he sang to himself.

Rock body back and forth.

Refrain

    A snippety-snappety,

        Encourage children to say refrain each time.
    Hi-diddle-dee!
    A clickety-clackety,
    One, two, three!

        Clap hands on each count.

He cut and he basted, this wee little elf,
Because he was making a coat for himself.

Hold up imaginary coat.

Repeat refrain

The little elf rocked and sang all the night;
He stitched and he sewed till the morning light.

Rock back and forth and pretend to sew.

Repeat refrain

He borrowed some green from the grass on the ground,

Cup hands.
From a nut on the tree he borrowed some brown.

Pointer finger and thumb together.

Repeat refrain

His coat was all done and he scampered away,

Motion of fingers running.
Singing his song that was happy and gay.

Repeat refrain

The Fairies' Wash Day

This is the fairies' wash day,
With acorn cups for tubs,
> Cup hands.
And tiny leaves for wash boards.
> Show palms.
Each fairy rubs and rubs.
> Motion of scrubbing.
The fairy sheets so white and fine
Upon the grass are drying.
> Motion of spreading.
The spider spins a line for them,
> Twirl finger.
And now the clothes are drying.

—*Maude Burnham*

● This rhyme can be used as a
relaxation activity.

Flannelboard figures needed
are five fairies.

Said This Little Fairy

Said this little fairy, "I'm as tired as can be."
> Point to first finger.
Said this little fairy, "My eyes can hardly see."
> Point to second finger.
Said this little fairy, "I'd like to go to bed."
> Point to third finger.
Said this little fairy, "I want to rest my head."
> Point to fourth finger.
Said this little fairy, "Come, climb the stairs with me."
> Point to thumb.
One, two, three, four, five; they tiptoed
> Point to each finger in turn.
Just as still as still could be.

The Owl and the Brownies

An owl sat alone on the branch of a tree,
>Fold hands.

And he was as quiet as quiet could be.
>Whisper.

It was night and his eyes were round like this.
>Make circles around eyes with fingers.

He looked all around; not a thing did he miss.
>Turn head from side to side.

Some brownies crept up on the branch of the tree,
>Make fingers creep up opposite arm.

And they were as quiet as quiet could be.
>Whisper.

Said the wise old owl, "To-whooooo, to-whoooooo."
Up jumped the brownies and away they flew.
>Hands move behind back.

The owl sat alone on the branch of a tree,
>Fold hands.

And he was as quiet as quiet could be.
>Whisper.

—Maude Burnham

● This poem can be used as a readiness rhyme to prepare class for activity to follow. It can also be used as a Hallowe'en finger play.

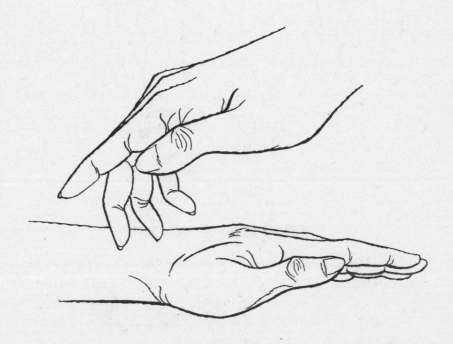

101

MOTHER GOOSE

The nursery rhymes from Mother Goose make excellent
material for starting children on finger plays. Four- and five-
year-olds will not understand the origin of these political
satires, but the lilting rhythms and gay rhymes provoke a
fascination in children of almost any age.

Two Blackbirds

There were two blackbirds
Sitting on a hill,
> Hold up both hands, thumbs erect, fingers bent.

The one named Jack,
> Wiggle one thumb.

The other named Jill.
> Wiggle other thumb.

Fly away, Jack!
> Bend down one thumb.

Fly away, Jill!
> Bend down other thumb.

Come back, Jack!
> Raise one thumb erect.

Come back, Jill!
> Raise other thumb erect.

—Mother Goose

Little Robin Redbreast

Little Robin Redbreast
Sat upon a rail;
> Thumb and little finger up.

Niddle-naddle went his head,
> Move thumb.

And wiggle-waggle went his tail.
> Move little finger.

—Mother Goose

This Little Cow

This little cow eats grass;
> Hold up one hand, fingers erect, bend down one finger.

This little cow eats hay;
> Bend down another finger.

This little cow drinks water,
> Bend down another finger.

And this little cow runs away.
> Bend down another finger.

This little cow does nothing
> Bend down last finger.

But lie and sleep all day.

—Mother Goose

● Continue the finger play substituting *Pointer, Middle Man, Ring Man,* and *Little Man* for *Thumbkin.*

Little Bo-Peep

Little Bo-Peep has lost her sheep,
  Hold up both hands with fingers extended.
And cannot tell where to find them.
  Hide hands behind back.
Leave them alone and they will come home,
  Bring hands from behind back and hold them up.
Wagging their tails behind them.
  Wiggle fingers.

—*Mother Goose*

Here Sits the Lord Mayor

Here sits the Lord Mayor,
  Point to forehead.
Here sit his two men;
  Point to eyes.
Here sits a rooster,
  Point to right cheek.
And here sits a hen.
  Point to left cheek.
Here sit the chickens,
  Point to nose.
Here they run in;
  Point to mouth.
Chin-chopper, chin-chopper,
  Move chin up and down with fingers.
Chin-chopper, chin!

—*Mother Goose*

Dance, Thumbkin, Dance

Dance, Thumbkin, dance;
  Wiggle thumb.
Dance, little fingers, everyone!
  Wiggle fingers.
But Thumbkin, he can dance alone.
  Wiggle thumb.
Thumbkin, he can dance alone.

—*Mother Goose*

Pat a Cake

Pat a cake, pat a cake, baker's man!
> Clap four times in rhythm.

Bake me a cake as fast as you can.
> Cup hands.

Pat it, and dot it, and mark it with B,
> Pantomime this action.

And put it in the oven
> Extend both hands.

For Baby and me.
> Point to member of class and then to self.

—*Mother Goose*

Little Miss Muffet

Little Miss Muffet sat on a tuffet,
> Make fist with thumb erect.

Eating her curds and whey;
> Pretend to eat.

Along came a spider,
> Make running motion with fingers.

And sat down beside her,
> Fingers move toward Miss Muffet.

And frightened Miss Muffet away!
> Show palms of hands.

—*Mother Goose*

Counting

1, 2, 3, 4, 5,
> Clap five times.

I caught a fish alive;
> Loud clap.

6, 7, 8, 9, 10,
> Clap five times.

I let it go again!
> Show palms of hands.

—*Mother Goose*

● Substitute names for *Baby*. Other letters which rhyme with *me* are *C, D, E, G, P, T, V, Z.*

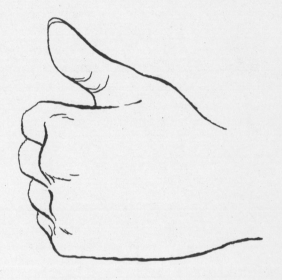

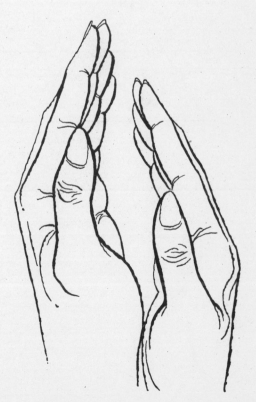

Little Boy Blue

Little Boy Blue, come blow your horn;
    Hold up clenched hands in a make believe horn.
The sheep are in the meadow,
    Hold up left hand and bend down fingers.
The cows are in the corn.
    Hold up right hand and bend down fingers.
Where is the little boy who looks after the sheep?
    Spread hands questioningly.
He's under the haystack,
Fast asleep!
    Place palms together and lay head to one side on hands.

—Mother Goose

Little Jack Horner

Little Jack Horner
Sat in a corner,
Eating a Christmas pie;
    Motion of eating.
He put in his thumb
    Motion of thumb pointing down.
And pulled out a plum,
    Thumb goes up.
And said, "What a good boy am I!"

—Mother Goose

Sing a Song of Sixpence

Sing a song of sixpence,
A pocket full of rye;

Place hands in imaginary pockets.

Four-and-twenty blackbirds

Flap arms.

Baked in a pie.

Make circle with arms.

When the pie was opened
The birds began to sing!

Two or three children whistle.

Wasn't that a dainty dish
To set before the king?

The king was in his counting house,
Counting out his money.

Motion of piling coins on top of each other.

The queen was in the parlor,
Eating bread and honey.

Motion of eating.

The maid was in the garden,
Hanging up the clothes,

Motion of hanging up clothes.

When down came a blackbird

Flap arms.

And snipped off her nose.

Pinch nose.

—Mother Goose

RHYMES FOR ACTIVE TIMES

Teachers frequently encounter a "wiggle" problem when nervous tension builds up in a group on those days of sudden weather changes or pre-holiday festivities. The rhymes in this section are excellent to use in such situations. They have no special theme and can be used at any time of the year.

Follow the Leader

Play a lively record that suggests lots of action, directing the children in movements in time to the music. These movements should be pantomimed. "The Parade of the Wooden Soldiers" or "The Teddy Bears' Picnic" are good records to use. All actions should be done to the rhythm of the music.

Here are some suggested actions for children to follow:

Touch a part of the face.	Flap arms like a bird.
Place finger tips on head.	Clap hands.
Make arms leap like a frog.	Twirl fingers.
Place finger tips on shoulders.	Touch knees.
Place thumbs in ears.	Draw a circle with finger.
Tap with finger on palm of hand.	Wiggle toes.
Hands on hips.	Tap with foot.

Wake Up, Little Fingers

Wake up, little fingers,
The morning has come.

> Fingers come up from doubled up fist.

Now hold them up, every finger and thumb.
Come, jump out of bed;

> Raise hands.

See how tall you can stand;

> Lower hands.

My, my, but you are a wide-awake band.

> Clap hands.

You have all washed your faces,

> Rub palms together.

And you look so neat.

> Fold hands.

Then come to the table and let us all eat.

> Motion of eating.

> Wiggle fingers.

Now, all of you fingers, run out to play,
And have a good time on this beautiful day!

> Clap hands.

—*Maude Burnham*

Fun with Hands

Roll, roll, roll your hands as slowly as can be;
Roll, roll, roll your hands;
Do it now with me.
Roll, roll, roll your hands as fast as fast can be;
Roll, roll, roll your hands;
Do it now with me.

Continue this action rhyme
by substituting these phrases:

Clap, clap, clap your hands.
Shake, shake, shake your hands.
Stamp, stamp, stamp your feet.

Open, Shut Them

Open, shut them; open, shut them;
Give them a clap.
Open, shut them; open, shut them;
Lay them in your lap.
Creep them, creep them slowly upward
To your rosy cheeks.
Open wide your shiny eyes
And through your fingers peep.
Open, shut them; open, shut them;
To your shoulders fly.
Let them, like the little birdies,
Flutter to the sky.
Falling, falling, slowly falling,
Nearly to the ground,
Quickly raising all your fingers,
Twirling them around.
Open, shut them; open, shut them;
Give them a clap.
Open, shut them; open, shut them;
Lay them in your lap.

—Traditional

Ten Little Finger Men

Ten little finger men,
> Hold up ten fingers.

Who will clap for me today?
"I will. I will," all my fingers say.
> Clap hands on "I will."

Ten little finger men,
> Hold up ten fingers.

Who will write for me today?
"I will. I will," all my fingers say.
> Draw circles in the air.

● Other verses can be used:
"Who will hide for me today?"
and "Who will put my toys
away?" This latter verse should
precede clean-up time.

Stretch, Stretch

Stretch, stretch away up high;
> Reach arms upward.

On your tiptoes, reach the sky.
> Stand on tiptoes and reach.

See the bluebirds flying high.
> Wave hands.

Now bend down and touch your toes;
> Bend to touch toes.

Now sway as the North Wind blows;
> Move body back and forth.

Waddle as the gander goes!
> Walk in waddling motion back to seats.

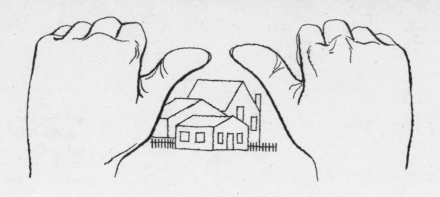

Hide and Seek

There's a funny little man in a funny little house;
    Hold up left thumb.
And right across the way
Is another little man in another little house;
    Hold up right thumb.
And they play hide and seek all day.
    Move both thumbs up and down.

One funny little man through his window peeps,
    Let left thumb move out from doubled fist.
Sees no one looking, then softly creeps
Out of his door so slowly—slow—
    Bring thumb out of fist gradually.
He looks up and down and high and low;
    Move thumb in different directions.
Then back into his house he goes.
    Bring thumb back into doubled up fist.

Then the other little man through his window peeps,
    Let right thumb move out of doubled up fist.
Sees no one looking, then softly creeps
Out of his door so slowly—slow—
    Bring thumb out of fist gradually.
He looks up and down and high and low;
    Move thumb in different directions.
Then back into his house he goes.
    Bring thumb back into doubled up fist.

Sometimes these little men forget to peep,
And out of their doors they softly creep,
    Move both thumbs out of doubled up fists.
Look up and down and high and low,
    Move thumbs in different directions.
See each other and laugh "HO! HO!"
    Bring thumbs toward each other.
Then back into their houses they go.
    Thumbs walk away from each other and return to doubled up fists.

—Traditional

Touch Your Nose

Touch your nose,
Touch your chin;
That's the way this game begins.
Touch your eyes,
Touch your knees;
Now pretend you're going to sneeze.
> Finger under nose.
Touch your hair,
Touch one ear;
Touch your two red lips right here.
Touch your elbows
Where they bend;
That's the way this touch game ends.

● This poem can be used to teach concepts of shape. Drawing in the air is a fine kinesthetic-tactile experience and should be practiced in kindergarten as a readiness device for writing in first grade.

Flannelboard materials needed are a felt circle, a square, and a triangle.

Draw a Circle

Draw a circle, draw a circle,
Round as can be;
> Draw a circle in the air with pointer finger.
Draw a circle, draw a circle
Just for me.

Draw a square, draw a square,
> Draw a square in the air.
Shaped like a door;
Draw a square, draw a square
With corners four.

Draw a triangle, draw a triangle
> Draw a triangle in the air.
With corners three;
Draw a triangle, draw a triangle
Just for me.

RHYMES FOR QUIET TIMES

The rhymes in this section are designed to induce relaxation. They can be used following a play period, or as a readiness technique preceding a new learning activity, or, perhaps, as a brief interlude of quietness and a change of pace in the midst of a hectic day.

Ready to Listen

Let your hands go clap, clap, clap;
>Clap hands three times.

Let your fingers snap, snap, snap;
>Snap fingers three times.

Let your lips go very round.
>Make lips round.

But do not make a sound.

Fold your hands and close each eye;
>Follow action indicated.

Take a breath . . . . and softly sigh:
Ah-----!
>Follow action indicated.

Readiness

Close your eyes, head drops down,
Face is smooth, not a frown;
Roll to left; head is a ball;
Roll to right; now sit tall!
Lift your chin; look at me!
Take deep breaths, one, two, three;
Make big smiles; hands in lap;
Make believe you've had a nap.
Now you're rested from your play.
Time to work again today!

● This can be used as a relaxation activity or to get children ready for a new activity following a play period.

Still Time

I've just come in from playing;
I'm as tired as I can be;
I'll cross my legs
And fold my hands
And close my eyes so I can't see.
I will not move my body;
I'll be like Raggedy Ann;
My head won't move;
My arms won't move;
I'll just be still
Because I can.

● This is a relaxation rhyme which can be enhanced by the use of a Raggedy Ann doll to demonstrate a relaxed body for the children.

Thumbkins

Mr. Thumbkin Left and Mr. Thumbkin Right
    Hold up both thumbs.
Met each other on a Sunday night;
    Move thumbs together.
Mr. Thumbkin Left said, "How do you do?"
    Wiggle left thumb.
Mr. Thumbkin Right said, "Fine, and thank you!"
    Wiggle right thumb.
They began to yawn and to nod their heads,
    Move hands apart.
And they went back home to their cozy beds.
    Place hands behind back.

● Continue, substituting the words *Mr. Pointer, Mr. Tall Man, Mr. Ring Man,* and *Mr. Wee Man.*

Stand Up Tall

Stand up tall;
> Children stand.

Hands in the air;
> Raise hands.

Now sit down
In your chair;
> Children sit.

Clap your hands;
> Clap three times as words are said.

Make a frown;
> Children knit brows.

Smile and smile,
> Children smile.

And flop like a clown!
> Children relax with arms dangling.

● Use this action game as a relaxation device. See *Talking Time*, p. 126, for information on the "sh" sound.

A Readinesss Game

Make one eye go wink, wink, wink;
> Wink one eye.

Make two eyes go blink, blink, blink.
> Blink both eyes.

Make two fingers stand just so;
> Hold up two fingers.

Then ten fingers in a row.
> Hold up ten fingers.

Front and back your head will rock;
> Rock head back and forth.

Then your fists will knock, knock, knock.
> Thump fists together.

Stretch and make a yawn so wide;
> Children stretch and yawn.

Drop your arms down to your sides.
> Let arms fall.

Close your eyes and help me say
> Close eyes.

Our very quiet sound today.
Sh . . . sh . . . sh . . . shhhhhhhhhhh!

I Wiggle

I wiggle my fingers,
> Wiggle fingers.

I wiggle my toes,
> Wiggle toes.

I wiggle my shoulders,
> Wiggle shoulders.

I wiggle my nose;
> Wiggle nose.

Now no more wiggles are left in me.
So I will be still as still can be.
> Fold hands in lap.

—Lucille F. Wood and Louise Binder Scott

● The music for this rhyme is included in an album of records called *Singing Fun,* recorded by Bowmar Records, Los Angeles, California and distributed by Webster Publishing Company.

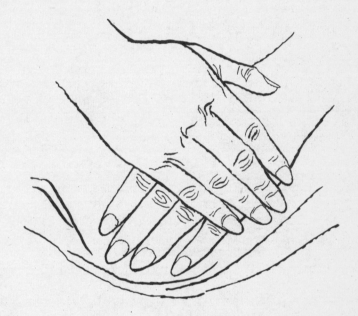

My Fingers

I stretch my fingers away up high,
> Lift fingers and stretch.

Until they almost reach the sky.
I lay them in my lap, you see,
> Fold hands in lap.

Where they're as quiet as can be!

Resting Time

Here's the baby's cradle,
Where baby likes to sleep.
> Lock fingers and rock them back and forth.

Here's a nest out in the barn
Where baby chickens cheep.
> Cup hands.

Here's the way I close my eyes.
And make believe I'm counting sheep;
> Rest head on two hands held palms together.

1, 2, 3, 4, 5, 6, 7, 8, 9, 10.
Now, I'm fast - - - - asleep - - - -!

● This poem can be used as a relaxation-readiness activity.

Flannelboard objects needed are a baby's cradle, a hen's nest, ten sheep, and a sleeping child.

THE SEASONS

Each season of the year has its own special appeal with its holidays, its weather, and its typical games. This section tries to catch the spirit of the seasons in its finger plays for Fall, Winter, and Spring. The rhymes are printed in that order.

There are no finger plays about Summer fun, since children are not usually in school during that part of the year.

The Snowman

Roll a snowball large,
>Arms make a circle.

Then one of middle size;
>Two pointer fingers and two thumbs make a circle.

Roll a snowball small;
>One pointer finger and thumb.

Use lumps of coal for eyes.
>Point to eyes.

Place a carrot for a nose,
>Point to nose.

An old hat on his head,
>Place both hands on top of head.

And for his necktie, tie around
His neck a ribbon red.
>Motion of tying ribbon.

A corncob pipe goes in his mouth,
>Point to mouth.

Some buttons on his vest;
>Point to buttons down front.

And there he stands so round and fat;
Of snowmen, he's the best!

● Flannelboard objects should be cut from colored felt. You will need three snowballs of different sizes, two lumps of coal, a carrot, a stovepipe hat, a red scarf, a corncob pipe, and three buttons for the snowman's vest.

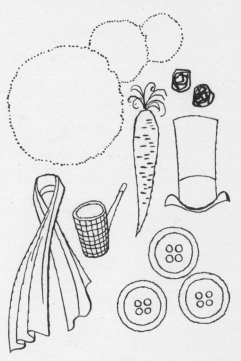

I Am a Snowman

I am a snowman, cold and white;
I stand so still through all the night;
>Stand up tall.

With a carrot nose,
>Point to nose.

And head held high,
And a lump of coal to make each eye.
>Point to eyes.

I have a muffler made of red,
And a stovepipe hat upon my head.
>Place hands on top of head.

The sun is coming out! Oh, my!
>Make circle for sun.

I think that I am going to cry;
>Start sinking to floor.

Yesterday, I was so plump and round;
Now I'm just a river on the ground.
>Sink to floor.

● This poem can be used for relaxation. With the flannelboard, use the felt materials listed under the preceding rhyme.

Making Kites

The winds of March begin to blow,
And it is time for kites, you know.

Here's the way I make my kite;
Watch and help me do it right.

I cross two sticks, so thin and long,
Cross pointer fingers.
Tied together good and strong;
Motion of tying.

A string I fasten to each end,
Pretend to hold each side of kite.
And across the middle to make it bend;

I measure and cut the paper gay,
Motion of measuring and cutting.
And paste along the edge this way;
Motion of pasting.

A ball of string to hold my kite,
Form circle with fingers.
When it sails almost out of sight;

And here's my kite all ready to go!
Hands outstretched.
Please, March Wind, begin to blow!

The Wind

The wind came out to play one day.
He swept the clouds out of his way;
Make sweeping motions with arms.
He blew the leaves and away they flew.
Make fluttering motions with fingers.
The trees bent low and their branches did, too.
Lift arms and lower them.
The wind blew the great big ships at sea;
Repeat sweeping motions.
The wind blew my kite away from me.

Raindrops

Raindrops, raindrops!
Falling all around;
Move fingers to imitate falling rain.
Pitter-patter on the rooftops,
Tap softly on desk or floor.
Pitter-patter on the ground;
Here is my umbrella;
It will keep me dry;
Hands over head.
When I go walking in the rain,
I hold it up so high.
Raise hands in air.

The Rain

Pitter-patter, raindrops,
Falling from the sky;
Wiggle fingers to imitate falling rain.
Here is my umbrella
To keep me safe and dry!
Hands over head.
When the rain is over,
And the sun begins to glow,
Make large circle with arms.
Little flowers start to bud,
Cup two hands together.
And grow and grow and grow!
Spread hands apart slowly.

Yellow Daffodil

Here is a yellow daffodil
That nods from left to right;
> Raise arm and weave back and forth.

Here are the leaves so soft and green
That guard it through the night.
> Hold up ten fingers, then bring
> them together and fold hands.

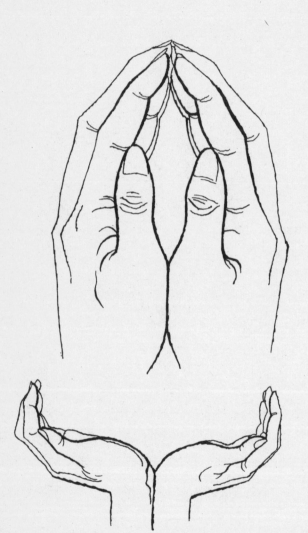

The Flower

Here's a green leaf,
> Show hand.

And here's a green leaf;
> Show other hand.

That, you see, makes two.
Here is a bud
> Cup hands together.

That makes a flower;
Watch it bloom for you!
> Open cupped hands gradually.

Relaxing Flowers

Five little flowers
Standing in the sun;
> Hold up five fingers.

See their heads nodding,
Bowing, one by one.
> Bend fingers several times.

Down, down, down
Comes the gentle rain,
> Raise hands, wiggle fingers, and lower
> arms to simulate falling rain.

And the five little flowers
Lift up their heads again!
> Hold up five fingers.

Purple Violets

One purple violet in our garden grew;
>Hold up one finger.

Up popped another, and that made two.
>Hold up two fingers.

Two purple violets were all that I could see;
But Billy found another, and that made three.
>Hold up three fingers.

Three purple violets—if I could find one more,
I'd make a wreath for Mother, and that would make four.
>Hold up four fingers.

Four purple violets—sure as you're alive!
Why, here is another! And now there are five!
>Hold up five fingers.

● Flannelboard materials needed are five purple violets.

Daisy Clocks

One o'clock, two o'clock, three o'clock, and four;
>Bend down one finger at a time.

I found a pretty daisy clock close by my door.
Five o'clock, six o'clock, seven o'clock, and eight;
>Bend down fingers.

I blew the petals one by one until the hour grew late.
I blew nine away, and then I blew ten;
>Bend down remaining fingers.

I picked another daisy, then, and started once again.

● For the flannelboard, cut a yellow felt center and ten white felt petals. Have a child remove the petals one at a time as the poem is said. Draw a clock face on the yellow center and attach movable paper hands with a paper fastener. Telling Time can follow the poem as a learning activity.

Flowers

Flowers tall,
>Let tall fingers stand up.

Flowers small,
>Let little finger and thumb stand up.

Count them one by one,
Blowing with the breezes
In the springtime sun!
1, 2, 3, 4, 5.
>Touch each finger as you count.

● Flannelboard materials needed are five flowers on green stems. Three of the flowers should have short stems and two should have long stems.

Pretending

I like to pretend that I am a rose
    Cup hands.
That grows and grows and grows and grows.
    Open hands gradually.
My hands are a rosebud closed up tight,
    Close hands.
With not a tiny speck of light.
Then slowly the petals open for me,
    Let hands come apart gradually.
And here is a full-blown rose, you see!

● Flannelboard materials needed are five May baskets, two of which should be yellow and one pink and blue.

Five Little May Baskets

Five little May baskets waiting by the door;
    Hold up five fingers.
One will go to Mrs. Smith, then there will be four.
    Bend down one finger.

Four little May baskets, pretty as can be;
One will go to Mrs. Brown, then there will be three.
    Bend down one finger.

Three little May baskets, one is pink and blue;
It will go to Mr. Jones, then there will be two.
    Bend down one finger.

Two little May baskets, yellow as the sun;
One will go to Mr. Black, then there will be one.
    Bend down one finger.

One little May basket; oh, it's sure to go
To my own dear mother, who's the nicest one I know.
    Cup hands to form basket.

TOYLAND

Toyland, in the music of Victor Herbert, is dear-little-girl-and-boy land, but it belongs to children in any language, including the language of finger plays.

● Use this poem for dramatic play and have children dramatize riding bicycles.

My Bicycle

One wheel, two wheels on the ground;
  Revolve hand in forward circle to form each wheel.
My feet make the pedals go round and round;
  Move feet in pedaling motion.
Handle bars help me steer so straight,
  Pretend to be steering a bicycle.
Down the sidewalk, through the gate.

● Flannelboard materials needed are five wooden soldiers.

Five Wooden Soldiers

Five wooden soldiers standing in a row;
  Hold up five fingers.
Look out! Look out! Down they go!
Down goes little man,
  Bend down little finger.
Down goes ring man,
  Bend down ring finger.
Down goes middle man,
  Bend down middle finger.
Down goes pointer,
  Bend down pointer finger.
Down goes thumbkin;
  Bend down thumb.
All five soldiers, lying just so!

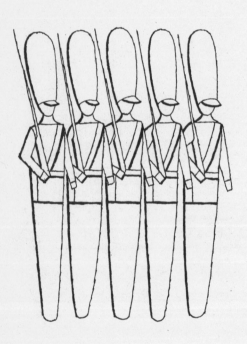

● Use this poem as a readiness device. It can be used to show children the difference between relaxation and tension.

I Am a Top

I am a top all wound up tight;
  Clasp hands tightly together.
I whirl and whirl with all my might;
  Make both hands wind around each other fast.
And now the whirls are out of me,
So I will rest as still as can be.
  Fold hands.

Three Balls

Here is a big, round, bouncy ball.
<small>Make circle with arms.</small>
I bounce it, 1, 2, 3.
<small>Motion of bouncing.</small>
Here is a ball for throwing.
<small>Make circle with thumbs and pointer fingers.</small>
I can catch it,
Watch and see.
<small>Pretend to catch ball.</small>
Here is a ball for rolling;
<small>Cup hands.</small>
Please roll it back to me.
<small>Pretend to roll ball.</small>
Bouncing;
<small>Action.</small>
Throwing;
<small>Action.</small>
Rolling balls;
<small>Action.</small>
Let's count them: 1, 2, 3!

Let's Make a Ball

A little ball,
<small>Make a circle with pointer finger and thumb.</small>
A bigger ball,
<small>Make a circle with both pointer fingers and thumbs.</small>
A great big ball I see;
<small>Make large circle with arms.</small>
Now, let's count the balls we've made;
1, 2, 3.
<small>Repeat action of first three lines.</small>

—Traditional

● Flannelboard materials needed are three colored felt circles of various sizes.

Bounce and Catch It

Bounce and catch it,
Bounce and catch it,
Bounce and catch the ball;
Bounce and catch it,
Bounce and catch it,
Do not let it fall!

● Have each child pretend to bounce a ball, clapping his hands as he catches it.

● The teacher may say the first three lines and the children the last line. Use this poem as a readiness activity.

● This finger play helps to teach the concepts of small and large. Let children draw balloons and color them. Have kindergarten children draw circles in the air with you. This activity will help prepare them for the round strokes they will get later in manuscript writing.

● This is an excellent poem for teaching the difference between relaxation and tension. A real puppet can be used to demonstrate the actions before they are tried out by the children.

Jack-in-the-Box

Jack-in-the-box
Sits so still;
> Children hide faces in their arms.

Will you come out?
Yes, I will!
> Children sit up tall.

—Unknown

My Balloon

Here I have a new balloon.
> Make circle with thumb and pointer finger.

Help me while I blow;
Small at first, then bigger,
> Make circle with thumbs and pointer fingers.

Watch it grow and grow.
> Make circle with arms.

Do you think it is big enough?
Maybe I should stop;
For if I give another blow,
My balloon will surely POP!
> Clap hands.

I'm a Little Puppet Clown

I'm a funny little puppet clown
When my strings move up and down.
> Bend at knees and go down and up.

First, I'll stand up,
Then I'll fall down.
> Sink to floor.

I'm a funny little puppet clown.

I'm a funny little puppet gay.
Move my strings and watch me play.
> Repeat above action.

Now I'm stiff.
> Stand tall, arms at sides.

Now I'm tall.
> Stretch on tip-toes.

Let go of my strings, and I will fall.
> Sink to floor.

Fun at the Playground

Climb the ladder, and down we slide;
> Motion of sliding.

Then on the teeter-totter we ride.
> Motion of hands going up and down.

Swinging, swinging, way up high,
> Swing arms back and forth.

Stretching, stretching to touch the sky.
> Stretch arms as high as possible.

Around we go on the merry-go-round,
> Stand and turn in a circle.

Having fun at our playground.

See-Saw

See-saw, see-saw,
> Hold out arms.

Up and down we go;
> Move arms up and down.

See-saw, see-saw,
High and then down low;
> Move arms up and down.

See-saw, see-saw,
Fun as you can see;
> Move arms up and down.

See-saw, see-saw,
Play the game with me;
> Move arms up and down.

See-saw, see-saw,
See-saw-see.

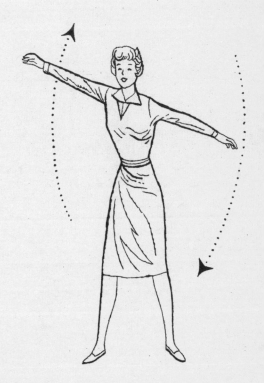

Alphabetical Index